The Powers of Hypnosis

THE BOUNDARIES OF KNOWLEDGE

The Powers of Hypnosis

JEAN DAUVEN

Translated from the French by
JOYCE E. CLEMOW

Stein and Day / *Publishers* / New York

First STEIN AND DAY PAPERBACK edition, 1971

First published in 1969

as Les Pouvoirs de l'hypnose

This edition has been somewhat condensed

from the French edition.

Library of Congress Catalog Card No. 71-87948

Designed by Bernard Schleifer

Printed in the United States of America

Stein and Day/*Publishers*/Scarborough House

Briarcliff Manor, N.Y. 10510

ISBN 0-8128-1391-X

SECOND PRINTING, 1976

Contents

Appendixes

It would not be very difficult to show that the further man advances in the conquest of what we must call his secondary powers, which are of a mechanical nature, the more he regresses in the possession of his primary powers, which are of an intuitive nature, and thus he is constantly being weakened.

C. F. RAMUZ

Preface

Why is Hypnosis Condemned?

I CONSIDER it an honor to introduce this study of hypnotism because in my opinion it is one of the most complete and thorough works that I have read on this subject in the past fifteen or twenty years. It is especially noteworthy because of the author's broadminded views and because of the extensive ground that he covers. This is more than a book about hypnosis; it is a work in which the phenomenon of hypnosis and its problematic nature have been placed back into a vast system of cultural coordinates. Thus it becomes possible to evaluate this problem precisely, not only from a historical point of view but also in relation to other psychological and philosophical problems, both past and present.

Although it is true that hypnosis is generally considered as having nothing occult about it and that men of science can now make a study of it without fear of compromising themselves, hypnosis still continues to pose important questions. It can in no way be treated as a mere chapter of psychology or neurophysiology.

Recalling the fluctuations in popularity that hypnosis has undergone, its periodic condemnations, those times when it was respected and those when it fell into disrepute, is sufficient to convince us that the subject arouses fear, even if it is absurd to equate it with magic or witchcraft or any other activity that science has relegated categorically to the realm of superstition and old wives' tales. The fact that hypnosis, when used by qualified persons, is no longer considered an occult activity is proved by the abundant amount of literature that has accumulated since World War II, the numerous convincing, verified results obtained by specialists in clinics and laboratories, and finally by the recognition of its therapeutic value by eminently qualified medical groups. In 1958 the American Medical Association (AMA) approved a report on the medical use of hypnosis. While pointing out that some aspects of hypnosis still remain unknown and controversial, the AMA declared that continued research on the subject was to be encouraged. Immediately after this, the British Medical Association expressed a similar opinion. In Italy several years ago the Italian Medical Association for the Study of Hypnosis (AMISI) was founded, bringing together psychiatrists, psychologists, and doctors of various specialties.

This volume broadly illustrates the various present-day applications of hypnosis in medicine and psychology. The principal fields of medical application are surgery, obstetrics, and odontology. The emphasis in this book will be on its importance in psychotherapy.

More and more, hypnosis is finding new uses in psychotherapy. Before the advent of psychoanalysis at the end of the nineteenth century, it was believed possible to make even serious neurotic symptoms disappear by peremptorily giving the hypnotized subject the required suggestions. But the hypnotists of those days were unaware of the idea of unconscious psychic conflict (and occasionally some hypnotists today seem unaware of this); the fact that most neuroses and psychosomatic disturbances have a structure whose roots penetrate deep into the unconscious remained in obscurity until Freud. Trying to obliterate the obvious aspects of a neurosis while leaving its roots intact would be equivalent to mowing the bad grass of a field and neglecting the vital part that continues to proliferate underground. More than once it has been noted that if hypnotic suggestion does succeed in making a psychoneurotic symptom disappear, often another more serious type of neurotic disturbance (or a psychosomatic ailment) appears in the patient after a while.

It is for this reason that supporters of psychotherapeutic hypnosis are careful not to use it superficially, as was the case eighty or ninety years ago. In psychotherapy today hypnosis serves mainly to weaken the inhibitive barriers that prevent the subject from allowing the roots of his inner problem from reaching his conscious mind. This type of intervention is known as "hypnoanalysis" or "facilitated analysis," and the procedure, which consists of diminishing psychic resistance and taking a conscious hold of what was unconscious, is essentially the same as that used in psychoanalysis.

Hypnosis can be used in some cases to shorten the length of treatment and to exploit all the possibilities of analytical psychotherapy. It has also proved itself in less serious cases of psychic disorder and is of use in transmitting direct suggestions (when this can be done with absolute security), in provoking an active re-elaboration of a traumatic experience, and in temporarily appeasing states of panic and extreme anxiety. These hypnotic interventions are used in conjunction with psychotherapeutic treatment when it is necessary to overcome certain blocks or specific resistances.

AN ENIGMA

In spite of its increasing acceptance in the medical and medicopsychological fields, it cannot be denied that hypnosis still has many unknown factors. There is an enigma about hypnosis that differs essentially from the unresolved problems of contemporary science. Our main purpose here will be to outline the salient aspects of this enigma and point out, where possible, the underlying causes of it.

In the first place, scientific interpretation of hypnotic phenomena is still extremely controversial. Even its designation is ambiguous. The term "hypnosis" is derived from the Greek *ypnos,* meaning sleep. But hypnosis is not a real sleep because the hypnotized subject does not sleep, nor does he dream. He does what the hypnotist tells him. He can talk and reason. Electroencephalograms recording the brain activity of a hypnotized person differ from those recording the brain activity of a sleeping man.

As for the general theories of hypnosis, at least five or six contradict one another. According to some, hypnosis is a phenomenon that can only be described in psychopathological terms.

Others link hypnosis with histological or even biochemical modifications of the central nervous system. Soviet neurologists and the exponents of the Pavlovian school interpret hypnosis as a specific excitation of certain cerebral regions and a relative depression of the other zones of the brain. It has been maintained that a subject in a hypnotized state behaves in the manner that he believes a hypnotized person *should behave,* that is, in conformity with a given model, as though he wants to satisfy the hypnotist by saying and doing what the latter expects. Even today some people maintain tthat hypnosis is only a state of hypersuggestibility in which the suggestions are accepted and carried out with infinitely more style than in the waking state.

The theory that considers hypnosis the result of a personality dissociation was one of the most popular theories fifty years ago and still has some advocates today. Finally, according to the psychoanalytical school of thought, hypnosis provokes a partial regression in the subject toward a state of infantile dependence and credulity. The hypnotist then represents for him an almost omnipotent image of paternal authority in whom he blindly trusts with no possibility of criticizing him. Some psychoanalysts have tried to combine the existing theories that are in agreement with classical psychoanalysis with the propositions of contemporary neurophysiologists of the Pavlovian school. The works of the Montreal school on sensory deprivation have been used to throw light on the notion of sensory "isolation," in which the hypnotized person finds himself and which is accompanied or followed by typical regressive phenomena. Hypnotic regression is the backward movement of the subject's personality toward levels that are less adult and more infantile; it is believed to be due partly to the specific, close relationship between the hypnotist and the subject and partly to certain physical conditionings of sensory restriction whose modes of action should be described in neurophysiological terms rather than in strict psychological terms.

Gil and Brenman, whose contributions to the psychoanalytical and psychodynamic interpretation of hypnosis are among the most important, conclude by defining hypnosis as a "sort of regressive process which can be set off by a reduction in ideational and sensorimotor activity or by the creation of an archaic relationship with the hypnotist." In actual fact, the hypnotist utilizes both procedures. The techniques producing hypnosis belong to two main types, which are not mutually incompatible: techniques based on stimulations and conditioning of a purely physical and mechanical kind, such as monotonous and rhythmic stimulations of a visual or auditory nature, and procedures based on a special interpersonal relationship that the hypnotist tries to establish and maintain. In the final analysis, these relationships place the hypnotized subject in a condition of extreme dependence, which was very correctly interpreted by the authors of the psychoanalytical school (Ferenczi, for example).

THE MOTIVES OF THE HYPNOTIZED PERSON

In spite of recent contributions and interpretations, no one has yet been able to describe the personality changes or cerebral modifications of a hypnotized individual with absolute scientific precision. In particular, no neurologist or neurophysiologist is ready to show in scientifically valid terms what happens to a subject in a state of hypnosis, for example, when his sensitivity to pain disappears in a certain clearly demarcated part of his body, with the result that stimulations normally of a highly painful intensity no longer produce the slightest effect, while beyond these fixed boundaries a mere pin prick continues to provoke normal neurophysiological reactions.

First, let us consider the subconscious reasons arousing interest in hypnotic phenomena, The motives causing not only laymen but also some scientists to become interested in hypnosis and to practice it are frequently, if not always, quite different from those that lead them to more orthodox activities. It is unquestionable that dreams of domination play a role in their motives; likewise a need to marvel, a desire for power, social or sexual aspirations, and, to a certain extent, a desire to feel despotic, demiurgic, or godlike. As for the motives of the subject, it has often been noted in psychological analysis that those subjects who willingly undergo hypnosis display a certain passiveness or passivo-masochism. Some men had homosexual tendencies deeply buried in their unconscious minds and showed partial analogies with female prototypes. Occasionally the hypnotist and the hypnotized person seemed to form a "complementary neurotic couple," where the more or less sadistic dreams of domination of the one corresponded to a masochistic desire to be dominated on the part of the other.

Among scientists there are various cases where the investigator's interest in hypnosis was intense at first, then decreased gradually or even disappeared abruptly. It is certain that negative and irrational motives were influential. But what is the reason for these ardent bursts of enthusiasm followed by an abrupt loss of interest?

The case of the famous English doctor John Elliotson (1791–1868), chairman of the Royal Medical and Surgery Society, is typical in this respect. In the middle of the last century, Elliotson performed major surgical operations under hypnosis, including the amputation of limbs. Some years later he suddenly declared that the hypnotic techniques "no longer possesed the power to remove pain." He did not explain the reason for this apparent "loss of power," but merely repeated, "It's a mystery." It goes without saying that this occasional, inexplicable disappearance of a proven efficacy is only one of the factors that, at various stages in the history of hypnotism, have discouraged and alienated scientists and compelled them to interest themselves in other therapies.

The modern interest in hypnosis dates back a little more than a century, but its beginnings go back to the final years of the eighteenth century, to the work of Mesmer and the advent of what was then called "animal magnetism" or mesmerism. If we wish to limit the history of hypnotism to its scientific phase, 1843 marks the date. In that year the English physician James Braid published his work *Neurhypnology* and introduced the term "hypnotism" into the language. How then do we explain the fact that this phenomenon regained popularity only a few years ago after a period of neglect lasting almost fifty years, from the beginning of this century until World War II?

Hypnosis has experienced success and disrepute more than once since the last century, and only today we are becoming aware of its strange, changing destiny. The reasons that have led us to be wary of it are usually the following: Since its origin,

Hypnotism began with Mesmer—*Holzapfel*

during each of its periods in vogue hypnosis has always been compromised by its share of charlatanism, comedy, and occultism. And every time this has disgusted and alienated scientists and serious professionals. We must add that hypnosis has not always kept its promises, as is illustrated in Elliotson's case. Here is another more famous example, that of Freud. He abandoned the hypnotic technique, considering it inadequate and untrustworthy, and introduced other methods for psychological investigation and psychotherapy, until he finally succeeded in formulating and perfecting psychoanalytical procedures. Psychology and psychotherapy today employ fundamental principles of knowledge and action that the hypnotists of the nineteenth century could not even have begun to imagine. As far as anesthesic applications of hypnosis are concerned, chemicopharmaceutical anesthesia has been so greatly refined that hypnotic anesthesia is ranked superfluous.

PSYCHIC BARRIERS

All these reasons, however, do not adequately explain the periodic eclipses in the popularity of hypnosis. There is in hypnosis something different, something that escapes ordinary scientific observation, yet is of a nature to attract and repel, in subtle ways and at deep levels, the attention and approval of men and scientists.

In order to comprehend the more specific, deeply concealed reasons for the various "deaths and resurrections" of hypnosis, we must delve into the psychology of the innermost being. The person who witnesses the astonishing phenomena of hypnosis experiences two reactions. One is conscious. The other is more subtle and unconscious. The first is a mixture of enthusiasm, stupefaction, and desire to investigate thoroughly such an extraordinary, thrilling phenomenon. The deeper reaction is quite different. Hypnosis proves that an individual in perfect physical and mental health can become the passive instrument of psychological forces that dominate him and that he is incapable of controlling. It shows that hypnotic commands temporarily destroy certain essential distinctions, for example, the difference between reality and unreality, or between true and false. These distinctions form the pivots of our whole life and psychic security. Thus, through hypnosis man can suddenly be confronted with his innermost self as well as with all the power and irrationality that exists in him. When confronted with these more or less short-lived revelations, the reaction of our psychic apparatus, psychoanalysis has taught us, is to mobilize "defense mechanisms."

Every psychoanalyst knows that when faced with alarming psychic phenomena, we defend ourselves automatically and unconsciously in various ways: by forgetting, refusing, minimizing, isolating, ridiculing, and so on. In other words, the ego of the hypnotized subject at unconscious levels, sets mechanisms for psychological protection into action.

What we have just pointed out would be an adequate explanation for some of the hypnotic "crises" even by limiting them to deep psychic activity and normal and pathological psychic dynamics, which psychoanalysis has now clearly elucidated. But there is more. Besides revealing disturbing and alarming psychic dimensions and realities, hypnosis forms a sort of bridge to other disquieting phenomena provoking psychic defenses. Today these phenomena are commonly called "parapsychological." In order to ascertain the value of this statement, we must go back into the history of hypnotism to the phase called "mesmerism" or animal magnetism.

Some of Mesmer's first disciples, the Marquis de Puységur and his two brothers in particular, noted that "magnetized" subjects from time to time showed proof of knowledge that they could not have acquired through normal channels. They could read the magnetizer's thoughts, perform imaginary voyages in space, and describe remote events that no one else present, not even the magnetizer, knew about. After a while these telepathic manifestations, or demonstrations of extrasensory perception as we prefer to call them today, became an accessory of magnetic seances and then of hypnotism in general. Therefore when the Society for Psychical Research was founded in London in 1882 with the principal aim of examining the real or presumed phenomena of mediumship, telepathy, and paranormal knowledge, no one was surprised that hypnotism was one of the subjects to be studied.

Even today most serious groups devoted to the study of parapsychology are still trying to determine if the state of hypnosis can provoke extrasensory perception. In some cases the results of their experimentation have been very positive and encouraging. But in the past, when magnetizers or hypnotizers found themselves confronted with a manifestation of parapsychological effects without looking for them, they were dumfounded and uneasy in the presence of these events. Seeing the frontiers of hypnosis expanding and extending in directions and to areas considered "taboo" by the majority of scientists undoubtedly contributed to turning away many people, particularly the so-called serious investigators, from this subject which was considered excessively dangerous.

Hypnosis apepars as a force that cannot be contained. Like a river that has overflowed every time men have tried to dam it up, so hypnosis has escaped all of man's best-intentioned attempts to classify it in one of the branches of acquired knowledge, to make it a chapter of a dissertation or a chapter in a university textbook. The failure of these attempts led men with good intentions to take a step backward and to be afraid.

ONE MUST BELIEVE

In hypnosis, as in other phenomena of normal and abnormal psychology, the inner frame of mind and attitude, considered *sub specie interioritatis* in particular, are of enormous importance, for they condition the phenomena themselves. Let us compare in this respect the characters of those who can hypnotize successfully with those who are incapable of doing it yet are convinced of the effectiveness of hypnosis and its practical value. It has always been observed that the best hypnotists are not scientists, nor are they men who have studied the phenomenon for a long time. The best hypnotists are often mere amateurs, more or less fanatical individuals who blindly believe in their capability to hypnotize other people. If these same people become more seriously and scientifically involved in hypnotism, or if they look for explanations for the phenomena that they themselves have set off or witnessed, often their former ability diminishes or disappears. Basically this is what happened in the case of Dr.

Elliotson. In reality, we know that hypnosis does not exist beyond and outside of hypnotists and hypnotized people. What happened to Elliotson was a change, a collapse of his own unconscious attitude toward hypnosis. Some subtle measure of self-criticism probably penetrated him, a doubt slipped in, and this is why, not "hypnosis," but *his* hypnosis no longer functioned.

It seems to us that these very reasons, which have from time to time caused the decline of hypnosis, make it one of the most exciting fields available today for scientific investigation. The very fact that hypnosis places us in the presence of contradictory developments of man's psychological and psychophysiological potentialities and gives us glimpses of possible extensions of the personality into still obscure and unknown directions constitutes an additional incentive to pursue our investigations even further. Hypnosis can be an extraordinary instrument, useful for increasing our knowledge and broadening our every day lives as thinking creatures. There is no doubt that psychoanalysis has advanced us considerably by extending our psychological knowledge. There is no doubt that parapsychology has decisively confronted research workers with the necessity of thoroughly examining and verifying phenomena that have been shrouded in a veil of incertitude for thousands of years, then reduced to the rank of superstition.

Hypnosis is at a sort of crossroads. Henceforth, the study of it should arouse a fervent interest instead of skepticism and fear. Showing by means of hypnotic phenomena to what extent, for example, unconscious motivations can influence our conscious psychic life; showing that beyond even the psychology that is accessible to psychoanalytical instruments, there is an obscure, latent paranormal zone of "available" psychic events to be explored and explained: these are the goals that should capture the enthusiasm of investigators and lead them to be interested in the vast problems thus brought to light. And Jean Dauven's work offers us a fascinating panorama of these very problems.

Emilio Servadio
President, Italian Psychoanalytical Society

PART I

THE HISTORY OF A CONDEMNED SCIENCE

CHAPTER I

The Exploits of Doctor Mesmer

LIKE those of magic, the origins of hypnosis go back into the abyss of the ages. Hypnosis can be found as a part of all manifestations of the unknown; it can be discovered whenever the powers generally accorded to man are transcended. In the recent past, retracing its history means going back over almost two centuries of error and blindness. In fact, few topics in medical science have given rise to so many disputes, have been submitted to so many learned tribunals, or have baffled so many eminent people.

Often, the bafflement was with good cause, because the problem was complex and the question confused. This was especially true in the beginning when hypnosis was known only in the form of animal magnetism, which at that time was linked with the idea of a universal fluid. By the time it was defined and had received a name, hypnotism had already overcome several condemnations.

In February 1778, when Dr. Franz Anton Mesmer arrived in Paris, the intellectual climate there was exciting. The king had restored to Parliament all its prerogatives that had been suppressed seven years earlier. And, encouraged by this generosity, Voltaire, now an old man, had just returned from a self-imposed exile that had lasted for more than a quarter of a century. His return was a symbol of the new age. The octogenarian was welcomed back with so much gaiety that he died four months later.

Mesmer had traveled to Paris after quietly leaving Vienna,

where he had made many enemies. But he probably would have come to France sooner or later anyway, because nowhere else would he have found a more broadminded audience for his theories. There was no other city and no other society like the Paris of those days. And possibly there has never been another era in the history of the world when the expansion of knowledge was accompanied by so much vivacity. The king was twenty-four years old and the queen twenty-three, and in the sciences, domains previously reserved for gray-headed academicians, young people everywhere were demonstrating astonishing abilities.

In their old age, the Encyclopedists saw the triumph of their monumental work, the last ten volumes of which had appeared in 1776. Rousseau died a few weeks after Voltaire, but the two main directors of the work, Diderot and d'Alembert, were still there to rejoice in the impetus they had given to science. The conciseness of their articles encouraged enlightened readers to extend their investigations further. As a result, discoveries flourished.

Mesmer too was convinced that his doctrine would orient science into new paths.

VIENNA WON AND LOST

Mesmer was born on May 23, 1734, at Iznang near Lake Constance in Swabia. Thanks to his father's position as a court hunter, he had been able to undertake prolonged studies. After completing his doctorate in philosophy at a Jesuit school, he had gone to Vienna to study law and music before becoming a medical doctor in 1776, at the age of thirty-two. In his thesis, *De influxu planetarum in corpus humanum* ("The Influence of the Stars and Planets on the Human Body"), he dealt with the correspondence between stellar phenomena and certain illnesses. In it, he bitterly deplored the foolishness of astrologers and, based on Newton's law of gravitation, affirmed that a coincidental relationship and even a cause-and-effect relationship exists between the phases of the stars and the state of men's health.

This thesis, defended by Mesmer before the Faculty of Vienna, should not be interpreted, as it often is, according to his memoirs and later works. In it, Mesmer puts forward his

Franz Anton Mesmer
(1734-1860)—*Corson*

findings but proposes no therapies. He deals only with stellar influences on the human body and their consequences. There is nothing absurd about this hypothesis, since neutrons can pass through three feet of living tissue and gamma rays can penetrate even further.

After he became a physician Mesmer married the wealthy widow of an imperial adviser, with the result that he was able to continue his investigations and lead an ostentatious life at the same time. When money began to get short, he decided to turn his knowledge to his own advantage. He was convinced that there exists a universal fluid. According to his theory, this fluid has properties that are uniform at every level of creation and is present in everything, producing, collecting, and sustaining as many magnetic vibrations as possible.

Mesmer's first well-known treatment was carried out in 1773 with magnets. He cured a young girl suffering from convulsions by placing a magnet on each thigh and a third on her stomach. Her treatment aroused a great deal of interest. But a Jesuit who claimed to have used the same method of treatment before Mesmer tried to discredit his success. Mesmer scarcely bothered to reply.

After giving considerable thought to the magnetic influence of living organisms, which he called "animal magnetism," Mesmer was now able to do without the magnets, which he considered superfluous, although not ineffective, and merely to rely on the laying on of hands as well as on the use of his own fluid in accordance with a method that he was gradually developing.

His reputation increased, and so did the number of envious people. He became fashionable and was consulted by the *haut monde* of Swabia and Switzerland. The Bavarian court summoned him, and there he cured the director of the Munich Academy of Sciences, Herr Osterwald, who was afflicted with an incapacitating amaurosis. Mesmer was unanimously elected a member of the Bavarian Academy.

On his return to Vienna, he decided to accommodate some of his patients at his own house in order to follow their progress more closely. In his house, which he transformed into a clinic, he restored the sight of an eighteen-year-old girl, Mlle. Paradies, who had gone blind at the age of four when she heard a noise at her bedroom door. In spite of her disability she was a famous musician. When the young girl was cured, her parents came to take her home, but she did not want to leave. Her mother slapped her; Mesmer intervened and the father drew his sword. Mesmer did likewise and forced M. Paradies to retreat. The mother fainted and the girl, who had become blind again either from the slap or from shock, remained with her healer.

Mesmer's enemies turned the situation into a scandal. Doctors were hostile to this rival who was straying from the teachings of the Faculty. The religious authorities, far from being grateful to Mesmer for wanting to give a scientific basis to phenomena that, up until then, had had an air of magic, considered excessively materialistic his theory in which man, the image of God, was subject to the same laws as all creation.

All Vienna joined in agreement. All envied the ostentation and success of this Swabian. Were they jealous of his amorous adventures too? Was it admissible that young Miss Paradies, the daughter of one of the emperor's private secretaries, was infatuated with this forty-year-old-man? Whether he had seduced her or cast a spell on her did not matter much. Why wait to deal with him? What were the police waiting for? And the clergy? And the court? Action had to be taken.

Life became insufferable. Leaving his wife to take care of the clinic—which was closed six months later—Mesmer departed for Paris.

THE SKEPTICISM OF THE ACADEMY

Mesmer rented an apartment in a townhouse in the well-to-do neighborhood of the Place Louis-le-Grand, today called Place Vendôme. He had great plans. In France, where all progress is welcomed, where minds are so open, he would be able to show scientists an aspect of science that was still unknown in the City of Light. The references that he brought, the printed accounts of Osterwald's cure, and his rank as a member of the Bavarian Academy earned him an invitation to read a report at the French Academy of Sciences. He went to the meeting, noted that the members of the Academy did not even listen to their own colleagues, and declined to give his report when the director, the king, invited him to mount the rostrum. The king who had introduced him to the distinguished assembly, then arranged for some of the members to go to Mesmer's house and witness his experiments in magnetism. There they were amused, and shrugged their shoulders. The theories of this Mesmer encompassed the whole universe. Only superstitious old women, they whispered, appeal to the stars, the saints, and demons to assert an influence over their fellow men. If he were not a doctor, he would have been suspected of heresy.

Indeed, he did succeed in making a person suffering from dropsy swell and become less swollen before the visitors' very eyes. "Nonsense!" they exclaimed. "It's the imagination playing tricks!" (But they did not say whose imagination.) And it is out of the question to take such nonsense into account, the good doctors countered, when they already have a whole series of remedies of unequaled variety for ailments of this kind. The *Précis de medecine pratique* ("Summary of Practical Medicine"), of which the third edition was published in 1769, just one year

The Academy of Sciences held that animal magnetism had no scientific basis—*Holzapfel*

before its learned author, Joseph Lieutaud, was appointed the king's physician, lists all these remedies with commendable far-sightedness, and at the end of the chapter on dropsy, he mentions the cantharides successfully used by a charlatan and that medicine would be very wrong to denounce.

MESMER'S TWENTY-SEVEN PROPOSITIONS

Mesmer had quickly understood the situation. It was going to be necessary to fall back on medicine and, as in Vienna, conquer by healing. This would be the best proof. However, in order to impress the doctors who had been badly informed by the members of the Academy whom he had disturbed, he decided to publish his doctrine. This treatise, published in 1779, is still famous. In Appendix A are the twenty-seven propositions summarizing Mesmer's thoughts. For almost two hundred years each generation has criticized or approved them, each according to its own enlightenment. No matter what opinion one holds about animal magnetism, it is generally acknowledged that Mesmer's propositions show the foresight of a genius.

There is no doubt that Mesmer is more fairly regarded now than a century ago, when Littré saw chemistry as the sole key to the science of life and life as nothing more than "perpetual combinations and uncombinations" consistent in every way with what happens in the test tubes of scientists. These words, though naïve today, were written in January 1855, at the same time as the young dean of the Faculty of Science at Lille, Louis Pasteur, was getting ready to prove the "catalytic action" of a multitude of living organisms, that exert an influence that chemistry has been unable to explain exactly.

Even today our physics includes sound principles admitting the existence of a "responsive influence between the heavenly bodies, the earth, and animated bodies," as stated in Mesmer's first proposition. There are also various conjectures about the exact nature of the universally diffused fluid mentioned in the second proposition. Both material and theoretical research have gone far beyond the most revealing analyses that Littré could have dreamed of, but despite all that, the mystery of primary causes has not been completely solved. But at least wise investigators have learned that science will probably never be able to explain everything.

LESSONS IN MODESTY

Mesmer's contemporaries did not take long to demonstrate that this foreigner had invented nothing. Was his fluid universal? Yes, but this had already been established in literature! And his magnetism was old hat. Whether it was mineral because of the magnet, or animal because of man's care, or combined with the "fluid" that constitutes both the medium and the agent for it, man knew about magnetism in all these forms since the earliest ages.

At that time, not much was known about *Ka,* the Egyptian principle of universal life, which was "a diffuse soul alternately regarded as the soul of the world and as an individual soul" (Robert Amadou). But a lot was known about the ancient Greeks. From Heraclitus (576–480 B.C.), who attributed the creation of man to a "spark of universal and divine fire," to Empedocles (fifth century B.C.), who described the universe as an immense system of attraction and repulsion; from Aristotle (384–322 B.C.), for whom everything that exists, both creatures and things, is united in the vital torrent of a nature in perpetual evolution, to the Alexandrian period of occultism and Hermetic philosophy, there was no modern concept that did not have precedents still being revived by alchemy, cabala, and magic. Fine associations indeed for a doctor interested in Mesmer's specialty!

In more recent times, there was Paracelsus (1493–1541), who attributed the human body with dual-purpose magnetic properties: one part attracts stellar rays to nourish the soul, the senses, and the mind; the other part is directed toward the stellar elements, from which it draws the very substance of the body, namely its flesh and its blood. It was noted—correctly—that many men had been inspired by the ideas of this enlightened Swiss. There was also Cardano, an Italian (1501–1576), whose name is given to a method of suspension in mechanics and who reported an anesthesia obtained with the help of a magnet; Goclenius (1572–1628), a Saxon doctor who claimed in his *Physiologia crepitus ventris* that he could heal by means of mineral magnetism; Van Helmont of Brussels (1577–1644), who treated by the power of the imagination; the Englishman Robert Fludd (1554–1637); and the Scotsman Maxwell (*Medicina magnetica,* 1679). In addition, there was Burgraeve, Helinotus, and Father Athanasius Kircher (1602–1680), a Jesuit from Germany who invented the magic lantern as well as the typewriter. Many others attached all sorts of virtues to the magnetism of man, thus putting within the reach of all this singular power that French kings used to exercise on gala days by touching persons afflicted with the "king's evil" (scrofula): "If the King touches you, God will heal you!" Louis XVI, however, did not prove to be very effective; out of two thousand scrofulous persons, he assisted only five or six—definitely a poorly functioning reign.

With regard to the "salutary crisis" that is provoked and directed by the physician (see Mesmer's twenty-fourth proposition), Mesmer's critics pointed out that the discovery of this dated back so far that it was already known at the beginning of the Hindu civilizations, in the temple of Isis, and by Pythia in a trance. It was experienced by all the hallucinated persons, magi, and sorcerers who, in all ages, in all climates, and in conscious or unconscious, real or simulated, neutral or provoked states of exaltation, prophesied and interpreted dreams while crowning themselves with supernatural gifts.

Mesmer was not lacking in experience, and we can assume that he had a very good idea of what he was exposing himself to by publishing his doctrine. But being also well versed in what today would be called publicity, he preferred to be the subject of discussion than to be unknown.

THE TRIUMPH OF THE TUB

The quarrels over Mesmer's propositions were secondary, however; his real battle was to defend his practice. His success was impressive. Patients flocked to him, and the apartment at Place Vendôme rapidly became too small, even though Mesmer had conceived a device that would allow him to treat thirty patients at the same time, namely a tub (*baquet*) (see Appendix

Patients being treated with the magnetic fluid of Mesmer's tub (*baquet*)
—*Holzapfel*

B). He had first formed this idea in Vienna, where he had a pond in his park. The device consisted of a vat filled with about a foot of water. Two or three layers of bottles of magnetized water were laid in convergent rows at the bottom of the vat, the neck of each bottle pointing toward the center. Bent iron rods were inserted into perforations in the lid covering the entire container so that they could be applied to that part of the body where the patient was afflicted. In addition, a rope, attached to the tub, was used for the same purpose and guaranteed a solidarity among the patients. Placed face to face whenever possible, the patients had to get as close to one another as possible and touch thighs, knees, and feet, thus forming only one body, so to speak, through which the magnetic fluid continually circulated, reinforced by all the points of contact.

CRISIS ACCOMPANIED BY THE PIANO

Overloaded with patients, Mesmer took on assistant magnetizers. In ceremonious silence they would group the patients around the tub, and after arranging the rope, would request them to form a magnetic chain by holding hands. When everything was ready, the sound of a piano could be heard from another room. Sometimes it was accompanied by singing and harmonicas, all creating a nostalgic atmosphere suitable for vague yearnings. And gradually the phenomena occurred:

> Some patients remain quiet and calm and experience nothing. Others cough, spit, feel some slight pain, local heat or general heat and they perspire. Others are shaken and rocked by convulsions, which are extraordinary by their number, duration and force. They have been known to persist for more than three hours . . . They are characterized by involuntary jerking movements in all the limbs and in the whole body; by contractions of the throat; by twitchings in the hypochondriac and epigastric regions; by visual disorders and rolling of the eyes; by piercing cries, tears, hiccups and immoderate laughter. They are preceded or followed by a state of languor and reverie and by a sort of despondency and even drowsiness.

After this clinical description, Jean Sylvain Bailly, a member of the Royal Academy of Sciences, emphasized the magnetizer's role:

> They are all so submissive to the magnetizer that even when they appear to be in a stupor, his voice, a glance, or a sign will rouse them from it. From all these results, it is impossible not to recognize that some great force acts upon and masters the patients, and that this force appears to reside in the magnetizer. This convulsive state is termed the *crisis*. It has been observed that many women and few men are subject to such crises. It has also been observed that these crises are only established after a lapse of one or two hours and that, when one is established, others begin soon and successively.

His assistants, all handsome boys, saw to it that the patients whose crises were becoming so violent that they were rolling on the ground and risking injury to themselves were carried into an adjoining room, padded on all sides. Meanwhile the master himself, olympian and clad in a coat of lilac silk, moved among them. He carried a long iron wand with which he would touch the bodies of the patients. Often he magnetized them with his eyes, fixing his gaze on theirs, or applying his hands to the hypochondriac region and to the lower part of the abdomen.

He also tried to obtain more violent results by making passes which, when prolonged, constituted "strong current magnetization." Erecting his fingers in the shape of a pyramid, he would pass his hands lightly all over the patient's body, beginning with the head, and then over the shoulders to the feet, sometimes down the front and sometimes down the back. He continued this process again and again until the magnetized person was saturated with the healing fluid and was swooning from pain or pleasure; it didn't really matter which. Both sensations were equally salutary.

Mesmer diagnosed the cause of some illnesses as obstructions. These circulatory blockages, whatever their nature, could involve both fluid energy and body fluids. According to Dr. Jean Vinchon,

> The conversion of fluid energy to electrical energy is often affirmed in the *Collection of Salutary Effects of the Magnet in Illnesses* [published by Mesmer in 1782]. The fluid energy is capable of being increased and decreased and of being preserved in receptacles that act as accumulators. It penetrates the human body but is stopped in its course by the visceral obstruction until this obstruction is removed by magnetism.

In the beginning, Mesmer had only one tub. Then, in order to accommodate still greater crowds, he opened a clinic at Créteil, then bought the Hôtel Bullion on the rue Coq-Heron, where he was able to set up four tubs, one of which was free (and under the direction of Antoine, the valet whom he had brought from Vienna). So many people flocked to this free tub that Mesmer decided to magnetize a tree at the end of the rue Bondy. Thousands of people with all types of ailments came and attached themselves to the tree with ropes hoping for a cure.

A TYPICAL CONSULTATION

The tub was the most striking aspect of Mesmer's therapeutics. He believed in the curative value of crisis and knew from experience that it could be obtained much more easily with groups than with individuals taken separately. During consultations he displayed intuition and diagnostic abilities that even his detractors have rarely contested. Several of his patients, out of gratitude for their recovery, published accounts of their cures. Among them is a detailed report of how he cured the learned Antoine Court de Gebelin, a royal censor and the author of *Monde primitif* ("Primitive World"), a lengthy work, one volume of which was published every year for nine years. In 1783 the subscribers who expected to receive the tenth volume were sent only a booklet; the author had not been able to work during the spring, having been "at death's door." The pamphlet extolled the praises of the doctor to whom he owed his life. Gebelin had not been able to get out of bed for months when a friend had introduced him to Dr. Mesmer, "that charlatan, that empiricist." He had heard so many bad things about Mesmer that he found it very difficult to have confidence in him. "Our conversation was cold," he admitted:

> "You have a very swollen leg."
> "Yes, very swollen, and the thigh is swollen too."
> "What do you think has caused this unfortunate problem?"
> "It is not surprising that this leg is swollen after spending five months in bed."
> "But the other leg is withering . . ."
> "Yes, and visibly so."

"Therefore the swelling is not caused by being in bed. Otherwise both legs would be swollen."

"So I was mistaken . . . But what is the cause of it?"

"Obstructions. They alone can prevent free circulation of the body fluids."

"That is possible. I have already been told that I have obstructions; and it is not surprising, as I was a very listless child and I had to work since the age of seven [he was now fifty-eight]. But I took nothing for it because I knew of no cure for an ailment of this kind."

However, Mr. Mesmer examined my leg, passed his hand many times over this excessive swelling and said to me, "My treatment could be very helpful to you."

"Fine, but I can't walk, nor can I climb into a carriage. So there is no hope."

Mr. Mesmer withdrew after telling me that it was imperative that I walk, get out of bed, bandage the lower part of my leg to help give it muscle tone, and drink cream of tartar.

Then follows the account of the cure. A friend took Court de Gebelin to Mesmer's place. He stayed there an hour and a half staring and almost regretting having come, asking himself, "What can all this do for me?"

In spite of his skepticism, he noted that he had come to Mesmer's that day "in slippers and with none of the buttons fastened at the knee of [my] britches," but that the next day he was able to put his shoes on and do up two of the knee buttons. So there had been an improvement in twenty-four hours. Then, all the symptoms gradually disappeared: the thirst after three days, the swelling of the thigh and the pain after seven or eight. He could walk to Mesmer's place; he was cured. He was now much stronger and less susceptible to fatigue than before.

Gebelin expressed his gratitude in a torrent of praise, about which we shall not go into detail here because, although he believed he was cured, the poor man died a year later of a kidney disease in Mesmer's clinic, which had just been moved to the Hôtel de Coigny, a little farther down the rue Coq-Heron. According to J.-P.-F. Deleuze, Mesmer knew that Gebelin was incurable. Furthermore, he had not told him that he would cure him, but simply that his treatment could be helpful. Very often, Mesmer felt obliged to take on hopeless cases, either out of friendship or in order not to annoy his rich clients. And people did not forget these failures, which they were happy to use against him.

At rue Coq-Heron, Mesmer had a large household: a doorman, a coachman, two valets, his faithful Antoine, a small orchestra that came every day, and two Swiss men to maintain order and direct the traffic outside. His expenses reached £20,000 a year, and his returns, £100,000 plus donations. One month of treatment with the tub cost ten louis.

Mesmer's greed has often been criticized, and not without cause. Since John Law, the Scottish financier who engineered the Mississippi scheme, had made speculation popular, the desire to get rich quick had become one of the shortcomings of the period. Voltaire had started his fortune with some lucky investments, Buffon was an ironmaster, Lavoisier a farmer general, and Beaumarchais a speculator. Mesmer's Parisian career was tarnished by all sorts of underhanded deals that made him even richer. He demanded a fortune for himself and a castle for his clinic if the people wanted him to remain in France. For him to confide his secret, it was necessary to start a subscription, with the fee set at one hundred louis a person. This succeeded, but without the official sanction of the medical body, which he wanted more than money or anything else, and which refusal left him dissatisfied, suspicious, and easily offended.

So, leaving behind a reputation for having occasionally been guilty of extortion and for going back on his word, Mesmer made a show of departing from France and set out for Spa, but Marie-Antoinette's Masonic entourage, the Duchess de Polignac, and the Princess de Lamballe intervened to make him return. He signed an acceptance, but had a disagreement with Maurepas, the minister (in spite of what they were granting him) and tendered his resignation in a letter, which, under a less good-natured sovereign, would have led him to the Bastille.

All this distrust was offensive to everyone. Mesmer became averse to all who did not believe in him. His chief rival, Dr. Charles Deslon, profited from this in a way that caused the downfall of both of them.

A RIVAL TUB

Dr. Charles Deslon, one of the regents of the Faculty of Medicine, had for a long time been Mesmer's most ardent and active disciple. As doctor to the Count of Artois—the future Charles X—he had aided Mesmer when the latter had first come to Paris, working with him, making his doctrine popular, and he had received much criticism for supporting his ideas. When Mesmer left for Spa, Deslon, worldly, elegant, and eloquent, took advantage of the opportunity to take his place. He had his own tub and had become experienced in Mesmer's methods.

When Mesmer returned, Deslon was exploiting magnetism in his own way. An attorney, Bergasse, and a banker, Kornmann, both fanatically devoted to the man who had restored their taste for living, had brought Mesmer back to head a philanthropic organization, "The Society of Harmony." The Society had more than three hundred members, but, even though Deslon had only sixty, among those sixty were a good third of those doctors who still repudiated Mesmer.

After listening to Deslon's defense of animal magnetism, the regents of the Faculty of Medicine had condemned him and ordered him to renounce his ideas or be struck from the roll of doctors. But success had gone to Deslon's head, and he believed he was influential enough to revenge himself for the insult he had received from the Faculty. He was confident that his revenge would place him way above Mesmer, and he wanted it made official by the highest authorities. Through devious means, Deslon managed to persuade the king to appoint a commission to rule on the effectiveness of animal magnetism as conceived and practiced by himself.

Mesmer was furious. His doctrine was going to be judged by the demonstrations of a dissenter, an infringer who knew his method only superficially.

Charles Deslon wanted a commission. He was given two. The first, appointed on March 12, 1784, included four doctors from the faculty of Paris: Borie, Sallin, Darcet, and Guillotin, and five members of the Academy of Sciences: Benjamin Franklin, Pierre Leroy, Jean Sylvain Bailly, de Bory, and Antoine Lavoisier. Borie, who died almost immediately, was replaced by Majault.

The delegation from the Academy was a distinguished one. Franklin, the inventor and statesman, was ambassador plenipotentiary from the United States; Lavoisier was the greatest French chemist and one of the twelve honorary members of the Royal Society of Medicine; Darcet had just published a report on electricity in the treatment of nervous diseases; and Leroy, guard of His Majesty's physical laboratory, belonged to various French and foreign academies. Bailly's titles were particularly impressive: he was Protector of the King's paintings; one of the forty members of the French Academy, a member of the Royal Academy of Sciences, the Academy of Inscriptions and Humanities, the Institute of Bologna, and the Academies of Stockholm, Haarlem, and Padua; and the mayor of Paris.

Deslon's second commission, appointed on April 6, was composed exclusively of members of the Royal Society of Medicine: Messrs. Poissonnier, A.-L. de Jussieu, Caille, de Mauduyt, and d'Andry.

But Deslon was not Mesmer, and he lacked Mesmer's prudence. Mesmer, in his recent proposal to treat twelve patients while twelve other patients were treated by conventional methods, had warned that "nothing proves conclusively that the doctor or the medicine cures diseases."

CONDEMNATION BY THE ACADEMIES

Deslon set as his goal the material demonstration of the existence of a magnetic fluid and its usefulness in the healing of diseases.

It was a failure. Deslon could provide no conclusive results, nor could a man named Jumelin, another magnetizer who had also developed his own method of operation. The members of the commission went to Franklin's house at Passy, where they often met out of courtesy for the American septuagenarian; they visited the private clinic conducted by Deslon, where they witnessed the effect of the tub firsthand; and they observed Jumelin's experiments at Majault's house. But nowhere did they observe anything proving the existence of a fluid. They noted too that all the experiments seemed to prove that the power of the operator was illusory and that the crises that should have been caused by the fluid often occurred at the wrong moment, without magnetization and solely because the patient believed he was magnetized.

Their conclusion was an unqualified condemnation:

> The members of the commission have ascertained that the animal magnetic fluid is not perceptible by any of the senses; that it has no action either on themselves or on the patients subjected to it. They are convinced that pressure and contact effect changes rarely favorable to the animal system and which injuriously affect the imagination. Finally, they have demonstrated by decisive experiments that imagination without magnetism can produce convulsions and that magnetism without imagination produces nothing. They have come to the unanimous conclusion that there is nothing to prove the existence of a magnetic fluid . . . and they feel obliged to add that the contact and repeated excitement of the imagination which produce the crises may become harmful.
>
> The spectacle of these crises is likewise dangerous, on account of the imitative faculty which is a law of nature. Consequently, all treatment in public where magnetism is employed must in the end be productive of evil results.

After the signatures there was an appendix stating that Mesmer was being condemned for the same reason, since his method was identical. In addition to this, there was also a confidential note from His Majesty concerning morality, in which he rather caustically compared the magnetizer's powers to the emotional attraction that one sex exerts over the other. It included a description of "the complete disorder of the senses" resulting from the intimate contact with the magnetizer and it explained how "some crises are due to a hidden but natural emotional cause to which women are more or less susceptible. These emotions accumulate and rise to their highest pitch, thus producing a convulsive state." Because of these descriptions, this secret note has since earned as many readers as the report itself.

The commission's report, drafted by Bailly, was delivered on August 11, 1784.

JUSSIEU'S REPORT

Five days later the members of the Royal Society of Medicine made known their conclusions. These were the same, but the commission was not unanimous. Antoine-Laurent de Jussieu had refused to sign.

Antoine-Laurent de Jussieu (1784–1836) was the nephew of Bernard, Antoine, and Joseph Jussieu, all distinguished scientists. Born, like them, at Lyon, he came to Paris when he was seventeen and worked with his uncle Bernard, a botanist, while he studied medicine. So, in 1770, after defending his thesis, which already inclined toward botany since it established a parallel between the structure and functions of plants and the phenomena of animal life, he gave up a career in medicine to become deputy professor in botany at the Museum. The titular professor was Lemonnier, the king's physician. It was A.-L. de Jussieu who, in 1774, set up an entirely new botanical classification in the King's Gardens. The deaths of Haller, Linnaeus, and his uncle Bernard made him, at thirty years of age, the foremost botanist in the world. He was a member of the Academy of Sciences from the age of twenty-five. Yet at the Museum he was only a botany assistant until the Revolution, and Lamarck, even though he too was a member of the Academy, was not even a subassistant. Jussieu became director in 1794.

Jussieu stated his reasons for refusing to sign the society's document in a third report, proving his courage and broadness of outlook. His perspicacity was not without shortcomings; as a magnetizer himself, he had occasionally made mistakes. But he was very advanced for his time. For instance, he wrote that the existence of a principle identified with fire and electric fluid cannot be denied, but that it is not necessarily the principle of animal movement, because, in abstract matters, everything can be admitted and rejected with the same facility. Noting too that "the fibers of the animal body have a property called irritability," he wondered whether this was an active principle or if perhaps it could be a property of matter that had become organic. A tricky question. To the credit of magnetism, he cited the successes he had witnessed. He criticized the excessive generalization of the fluid in the major theories, and urged methodical research carried out on what he considered the definite effects of animal heat, man's action on man, and of what he called "tactile medicine."

We shall come back to the question of the use of hypnotic "passes," because we would be deluding ourselves if we claimed that by "tactile medicine" Jussieu was referring to massaging. Massaging has a very remote precursor in rubbing, and Jussieu would not have made a fool of himself by pointing out the possible effectiveness of this.

Jussieu's remarks, however, had no repercussions, except perhaps on his career, until after the Revolution.

FORGOTTEN CHARLATAN OR MISUNDERSTOOD PRECURSOR?

So Charles Deslon was condemned. Mesmer was too, but he had just cause for scorning this tribunal that had not even heard his case. About the same time, however, a failure made him doubt whether he still possessed his magnetic power (or we could say mediumistic power): he had been unable to influence Prince Henry of Prussia. Until then, he had never had any doubts. This disappointment completely discouraged him and he left for London. Deslon, though still in the prime of life, lived only two years after his failure. Rising above his fate, Mesmer returned to his beloved forests on the shores of Lake Constance, "like a forgotten charlatan," it has been written, but this seems unjust. In reality, he was rather like a precursor, misunderstood for a long time, but whose theories survived the test of time.

Mesmer returned to Paris several times. He was in Paris on November 10, 1793, when Bailly, who had lost favor with the Crown, was executed. Mesmer imprudently took off his hat to salute the cart as it passed by. This gesture was not overlooked on his return to Vienna, where some of his forthright remarks with regard to revolutionaries caused him to be put in prison, then confined to his residence.

But France granted him a pension in 1802, so he had not left behind too bad a memory. He ended his days like one of Jean-Jacques Rousseau's characters, dividing his time between caring for the poor and worshipping nature. He was still very alert when in 1812, at the age of seventy-nine, the King of Prussia officially invited him to come and teach animal magnetism at Berlin. He declined the offer and it was Dr. Wolfart, the doctor to whom he had given all his documents, who occupied the chair at the university, then later directed a mesmeric hospital with 310 beds.

Three years later, on March 15, 1815, Mesmer died at Mersbourg on Lake Constance.

CHAPTER II

Fortunes and Misfortunes of Somnambulism

EVEN before Mesmer was condemned by procuration, animal magnetism in France was already performing wonders that were destined to have remarkable consequences. Three of the most enthusiastic disciples of Mesmer's secret society "Harmonia" (not a Masonic society) were the Puységur brothers, grandsons of the French field marshal. Each, in his own field, was making the new therapy known. The youngest effected some cures on board the frigate he was commanding. The middle brother organized a tub at Bayonne and promised to give £600, which he placed in safe deposit at the town hall, to anyone who could prove that his cures were not genuine. And the eldest brother, the Marquis de Puységur, was repeating Mesmer's experiments at Buzancy and, like Mesmer, magnetized an elm tree. This was a great success; the treatment was gentler than that of the tub and the crises were rarer and less violent. The placid peasant folk dozed off instead of getting agitated. The marvel was that one of them, a man called Victor, whom Puységur was treating for an inflammation of the lungs, went into a sort of trance and fell asleep, yet did not stop moving. And he spoke with an ease that he had never been known to have before, discussing his illness in a most amazing way. When he awoke he could not remember anything.

THE WORKS OF MARQUIS DE PUYSÉGUR

This happened on May 4, 1784. The Marquis de Puységur lost no time in defining Victor's entranced state, calling it "magnetic somnambulism." He gave the name "clairvoyance" to the intelligence Victor displayed while asleep, to his diagnostic accuracy, and to his prescience about the course of his own illness and later about the diseases of others. Furthermore, Puységur saw no limits to his clairvoyance, because while dozing, Victor could read thoughts, reply to them, anticipate orders, and carry them out in describing the vicissitudes of his own organs and the remedies that would be able to cure them.

Puységur published his observations immediately and he was to put forward other theories during the next twenty years. He was a gentleman of spiritual greatness who wanted nothing more than to serve humanity. His motto was, "Be willing and believe." Although he was very proud of his discovery, he did not claim to have surpassed Mesmer even in this field, because he was sure that the master must have been acquainted with somnambulism.

This is highly probable. Among the cures that he witnessed at Deslon's, Jussieu recorded in his report the case of a young man who looked for other patients and assisted them like a magnetizer while experiencing his own crisis. When he returned to his normal state, he could not remember anything and could no longer magnetize.

If Jussieu had been able to observe this unconscious activity several times while a member of the commission, how could Mesmer not have observed it too in so many years of practice? He no doubt mistrusted this state of activity during sleep, when every illusion becomes possible. He had neither defined it nor named it, probably because in his opinion it was only one of the elements comprising the "crisis." Intelligent people later came to believe in it, but in the meantime such an enormous amount of "marvels" and evidence had accumulated that it had become impossible to distinguish the truth.

Armand de Puységur founded a school. His works were confirmed by the experiments of Pététin, perpetual president of the Doctors' Society of Lyon. In 1787 this eminent man presented

The magnetized elm tree of Puységur, who defined "magnetic somnambulism"—*Holzapfel*

a woman who could see, hear, smell, and taste through her epigastrium and fingertips when in a cataleptic state. Then came seven similar observations. Pététin did not believe in animal magnetism, but he did acknowledge transposition of the senses, another mysterious, providential phenomenon for magnetizers—as if somnambulism and clairvoyance had not supplied them with sufficient material for performing miracles!

FROM DELEUZE TO DUPOTET

In France things evolved quietly and discreetly but very efficiently for such troubled times, until 1825. Numerous written works and countless experiments indicate that Mesmer's condemnation had cut short only official participation, for research, studies, and demonstrations were continuing, in both the field of therapy and somnambulism.

Both these aspects can be found in the voluminous *Histoire critique du magnétisme animal* ("Critical History of Animal Magnetism"), published in 1813 by J.-P.-F. Deleuze, librarian at the Museum and magnetizer in his free time. Deleuze had treated by making passes, but he still claimed that somnambulists possessed exceptional powers, thus corroborating Puységur's assertions.

In 1813 an abbot named Faria from Goa, a Portuguese enclave in India, was giving performances with an admission charge. He would gaze fixedly at his subjects, then order them to sit in an armchair and close their eyes. Then, in a loud voice, he gave them the command, "Sleep." The results he obtained were excellent. Moreover, Abbot Faria was a very colorful character, whom Alexander Dumas the elder portrayed as the man in the cell next to the one where the Count of Monte Cristo was a prisoner. Comedian that he was, Faria had understood that somnambulism has its roots in the subject's imagination.

After Faria's death in 1819, one of his pupils, Noizet, put forward the important psychological law that any idea firmly implanted in the mind tends to generate its own actuality. This doctrine, hinted at since the beginning of the mesmeric controversies, attributes the origin of the phenomenon called "animism" to the imagination and places it in the soul, thus opposing animism to "fluidism," which defines every "event" as a result of the universal fluid, the source of the operator's magnetic power.

In actual fact, these are two different phenomena. One is psychic, as is amply proved by the artificially provoked sleep. The other is physical and is still being fiercely contested and defended, since the existence of the magnetizer's fluid has never been proved with facts.

However, regardless of the medium, it was at the dawn of the nineteenth century that the first medical efforts were made to utilize the somnabulistic state obtained by magnetizing the patient. A dentist by the name of Martorel pulled a tooth painlessly in 1819. In 1821 Doctor Recamier used moxas to burn patients who had been magnetized by Jean de Sennevoy, the Baron Dupotet (1796–1881). Baron Dupotet used to perform experiments at the Hôtel-Dieu Paris, in M. Husson's apartment, and also at Salpêtrière with Doctors Georget and Rostan. And in 1820, Dr. Bertrand, a former engineering student who had become a doctor, started a public course in magnetism in which he emphasized the role of suggestion.

THE ACADEMY REVERSES ITS OPINION

The general board of directors for hospitals put an end to experimentation in the public clinics, declaring that patients were not research material—a position that cannot be censured.

As the risks involved in magnetism were small, investigators and enthusiasts did not give up. In 1825 a recently graduated doctor, Dr. P. Foissac, invited the Academy of Medicine to examine his somnambulists, whom he declared capable of diagnosing diseases "with inspiration bordering on the genius of Hippocrates." This was disturbing, so Husson was asked to draw up a preliminary report. His conclusions were favorable. They were discussed for two days before a court of inquiry was appointed, of which the same Husson was to be the chairman. But he was an unhurried chairman: it was six years before the results of the investigations were made known.

The investigators did acknowledge the existence of animal magnetism. They concluded that its effects, in most cases, were nonexistent and insignificant, and were caused by boredom, monotony, and the imagination, but that occasionally magnetism alone did produce results and these were "clearly established physiological and therapeutic phenomena."

The way in which these phenomena proceeded and their nature were clearly stated. But on the other hand, when the delegates from the Academy examined somnambulism and clairvoyance, they unfortunately showed themselves to be somewhat naïve. They accepted feats of second sight, diagnostics, reading blindfolded, divination, and prediction, which conclusions displayed an alarming lack of experimental method and a lack of critical judgment. It is true though that, with only one exception, the nine signatories of the report did not leave a shining wake in the medical arts. On the other hand, two of the three most eminent members appointed to the committee, namely Francois Magendie and Double, did not sign the report and did not take part in the inquiry. The Academy decided not to publish it.

THE END OF A QUARREL

Naturally the magnetizers were jubilant, interpreting the silence as an acceptance. But the quarrel soon began again. In 1837, another recently graduated doctor, Berna, proposed to demonstrate to the Academy extraordinary phenomena of magnetization, such as sight without use of the eyes, direct communication of thoughts between the magnetizer and the magnetized subject, and even thought communication through a door. A new and entirely different committee was appointed to investigate.

Emile Dubois-Raymond, the chairman, was as prompt as his predecessor had been slow. Berna had written on February 12. By July 17, everything was settled! Berna's claims were rejected. Somnambulism was denied, as was the very existence of magnetism—under the astonishing pretext that no other operator had dared to appear openly to request academic approval or censure. To strengthen his position, as if the summary condemnation were not sufficient, Dubois encouraged one of his colleagues, Burdin, to offer a prize of three thousand francs to anyone who could read in the dark without using his eyes.

This was a strange and even absurd way of getting around the question of animal magnetism. However, the Burdin prize was created, and because no one was able to win it by reading a book that was inside a box, the elite of the medical profession believed that they were correct in concluding that the magnetizer's claims were ill-founded and that animal magnetism constituted a false problem because, in fact, there was no such thing. Henceforth, they prohibited the examination of this problem in the same way the Academy of Sciences rejected any proposal to study perpetual motion and the quadrature of the circle.

Dubois could pat himself on the back though. Not content with having enlisted the prestige of the Academy to disconcert a presumptuous student, he had made this whole court of inquiry adopt his attitude of irritation when deliberation should have been the rule.

CHAPTER III

Fame and Disrepute of Hypnotism

THE ostracism of the Academy of Medicine did not impress anyone, however. The somnambulists, who were widely publicized in the newspapers, went about their business, reading the future, prescribing panaceas, and demonstrating their power in vaudeville performances.

But one magnetizer, the Baron Dupotet, did take offense at the official banishment because, prior to it, he had been one of magnetism's keenest exponents in the large hospitals. He had also been Husson's guide in his endless inquiry. The baron did not yield his position. When the opportunity arose, he went to England. His accounts of surgical operations performed on subjects who had been put into an induced sleep and who had thus suffered no pain interested Dr. John Elliotson, then at the peak of his career. Elliotson was a doctor of repute, teaching at the University of London. He was one of the founders of the hospital connected with the Faculty of Medicine and chairman of the Royal Medical and Surgical Society.

This great man did nothing halfheartedly. Fascinated by magnetism, he pursued his interest with zeal. He studied its surgical use as well as its action on the nervous system. When the university learned this, it forbade all mesmeric practices in its hospital so as not to be at odds with the established medical bodies of France. Elliotson was unyielding and resigned his position at the university. His name was dragged through the mud, but the results he obtained could not be denied, and in 1843 he started the journal *Zoist* to make his findings known. Public opinion was behind him, and many young doctors were too; in 1846 he was able to set up a "mesmeric hospital" in London. Several similar mesmeric institutions were then founded in the United Kingdom. At the hospital in Exeter, Dr. Parker claimed to have performed two hundred painless surgical operations on magnetized subjects.

MESMERIC SURGERY

However, it was at Calcutta that the most amazing feats were accomplished. James Esdaile, a Scottish doctor who was a great admirer of Elliotson, had been converted to magnetism there. He had never read a treatise about it but had simply gathered his information from a few articles. Then, in April 1846, he decided to use magnetism to reduce the pain of a man he was operating on for a hydrocele. Although his method was rudimentary, he was able to put the patient, a convict, to sleep, and the patient felt absolutely no pain either during the operation or after it. This story that began in a prison ended with the creation of a mesmeric hospital and a practice made up of rajahs and a hundred prominent witnesses. Esdaile's operating rooms became one of the sights of the city.

By the time he left Calcutta, Esdaile had performed more than two thousand operations, three hundred of which were major. We shall return later to the topic of surgery and to the successes and disappointments of this amazing practitioner whose contribution has often been ignored.

Meanwhile, something very important had just happened in England. In November 1841 a Swiss named La Fontaine had performed experiments in magnetism at Manchester. It was said that the priests of Naples tolerated him only on condition that he did not parody miracles by making blind people see and deaf people hear. According to some sources, he was received by the Pope. And we know that at the beginning of his British tour he magnetized a lion at the London zoo.

La Fontaine gave three performances at Manchester. James Braid (1795–1860), a Scottish surgeon living in that city, was present at the first performance, convinced it was all a hoax. He saw nothing to cause him to alter this preconceived view. How-

James Braid
(1795-1860)—*Holzapfel*

ever, Braid returned for the second experiment six days later and this time his attention was caught by a patient who was unable to open his eyes. Braid regarded this as a real phenomenon and was anxious to discover the psychological cause of it. At the third performance, he believed he had found the solution. He then made a series of experiments of his own. He put his assistant, his own wife, and a manservant to sleep. The assistant fell asleep in three minutes by gazing intently at the top of a bottle, his wife fell asleep in two and a half minutes by staring fixedly at the lid of a sugar bowl, and the servant also fell asleep in two and a half minutes. The servant had not been informed that this was an experiment in magnetism; he had simply been told to watch a pharmaceutical preparation without blinking. Believing that he had not put them to sleep but that they *were* asleep, Braid set forth the theory that "fixed gazing produced the phenomenon by paralyzing the nerve centers of the eyes and their dependent areas and by destroying the balance of the nervous system."

HYPNOTISM RECEIVES ITS NAME

Braid's explanation of magnetic sleep is questionable, but nevertheless we cannot overemphasize the importance of his discovery: he had proved that somnambulism is a state not necessarily requiring the personal intervention of an operator or even the action of a fluid.

He published his theories two years later and gave the name "hypnotism" to the nervous sleep that he was describing. As Joseph Ernest Renan pointed out, "It is a solemn moment when a new creation receives its name; for the name is a definite sign of its existence. It is through this name that an individual being or a collective unit becomes itself and not another."

From then on, hypnotism was no longer associated with magnetism. It became a material practice, and, as it required no contact between the hypnotist and the subject, the former grounds for complaint were no longer valid. And finally, hypnotism was no longer a part of the numerous demonstrations of a universal fluid. Thanks to Braid, hypnotism was on firm ground and there was now nothing to prevent it from remaining strictly scientific. Nothing—except the stubborn hostility of the official medical bodies, both in Paris and London. So, at first, there were many hypnotists discussing hypnotism from the stage but very few doctors experimenting with it.

In 1842 Braid offered to present a paper on the subject of hypnotism, followed by a demonstration, to the British Medical Association. This was refused, whereupon he decided to publish a book, *Neurhypnology,* in order to publicize his doctrine, which was currently called "Braidism." The proof that it was not without a future was that competition was already arising. A man named Grimes in America was proposing a verbal suggestion method, which he called electrobiology.

In France, Braidism was made known by Dr. Durand de Gros, who used the pseudonym "Dr. Philips" because he had been denounced atfer the December 2 coup d'etat. He also defended electrobiology and put forward his own ideas about it. These were published in his *Cours de braidisme* ("Course in Braidism") but were abstract and confusing. Some of his surgical operations that aroused widespread interest were to prove much more effective propaganda.

In 1859 the famous clinician Velpeau gave the Academy of Sciences an account of the incision of an anal abcess performed on a subject who had been hypnotized by Broca and Follin. The Academy listened to him respectfully. Animal magnetism, that outlawed phenomenon, had returned under the name of hypnotism just as Durand de Gros had come back under the name of Philips! A blaze of surgical operations followed, the most noteworthy of which was the amputation of a leg at the thigh by Dr. Guérineau of Poitiers.

LIÉBEAULT AND THE NANCY SCHOOL

It was a Dr. Azam from Bordeaux, an advocate of Braidism, who had led Broca to be interested in hypnotic anesthesia. And it was Velpeau's report to the Academy that had encouraged Ambrose-Auguste Liébeault (1823–1904), a country doctor from the Nancy region, to take up the subject more or less where Braid had left off, after Liébeault had studied various cases of rheumatism, epilepsy, neuralgia, and paralysis. In 1866, Liébeault published a book entitled *Du Sommeil et des états analogues, considérés surtout du point de vue de l'action du moral sur le physique* ("Concerning Sleep and Analogous States Considered in Particular from the Point of View of the Action of the State of Mind on the Physical State"). Only one copy was sold. On the other hand, he was curing patients by the hundreds.

In his village of Port-Saint-Vincent, this apostle who had elected to become exclusively a psychologist was treating mainly poor people by suggesting that they were feeling better. No diagnosis. No examination. He put them to sleep and, in a monotonous but penetrating voice, overwhelmed them with suggestions, mostly of a general nature concerning health, digestion, circulation, coughing, and so forth. Only a few of the suggestions had any relation to the patient's complaint. And that was all.

Suggestions, a running fire of suggestions, but also cures—a host of cures.

Liébeault's colleagues regarded him as a quack. A professor from the University of Nancy, Hippolyte Bernheim (1837–1919), came to expose him. Instead, he was converted. And soon, using all of his professional authority, Bernheim was performing countless treatments at the hospital at Nancy. The two men became friends and, at Bernheim's invitation, Liébeault settled in Nancy and the city became the center of a school whose reputation throughout the world was equal to that of Salpêtrière in Paris.

After Velpeau's report, people were anxious to forget the charges made by the Academy of Medicine. Earlier, in 1846, there had been this statement pronounced by Lacordaire at Notre-Dame: "Plunged in an artificial sleep, man can see through opaque bodies, name remedies that can cure, and he appears to know things which he does not know." But this homage to somnambulism in the extreme, and this lesson in humility for man in his ordinary waking state, had given rise to such a band of magnetizing priests that the Vatican reacted. An encyclical defined the use of magnetism in certain cases (an important restriction) as an "utterly condemnable, heretical, and scandalous deceit against moral purity." And in 1865 a jury at Var had condemned the vagabond Castellau to twelve years in prison for raping a young peasant girl after hypnotizing her.

Hypnotism could not be repudiated any longer.

CHARCOT AND THE SALPÊTRIÈRE SCHOOL

At Paris, thanks to Jean-Martin Charcot (1825–1893), hypnotism was to make rapid progress. Impressed by the demonstrations given by the Belgian Donato, who worked mainly on the stage, Charcot allowed his assistants to experiment with hysterical patients at Salpêtrière. His first four years of research culminated in the delivery of a report to the Academy of Medicine on the "various nervous states determined by hypnotism in hysterical patients." No one had expected that with his report magnetism which had previously been chased out through one door, was

Jean-Martin Charcot (1824-1893)
Poliopoulos, Réalité

now going to come back in through another. How could people not believe in Charcot's solid materialism? Yet, even though the Salpêtrière team did obtain some amazing results from their hysterical patients, they did not take all the desired precautions in their experiments. Eager to interest and anxious to please, the inmates of Charcot's wards did not want to disappoint him at any price. As hysteria and simulation often go hand in hand in patients who are unaware of it, such subjects can obviously produce excellent results.

Charcot and his associates progressed so enthusiastically that it seemed as though there was no stopping them. After thought transmission and long-acting medications, transference had been discovered. This consisted of making one patient's ailment pass to a patient suffering from hysteria. This instantaneous transfer, perfected by the neurologist J. F. F. Babinski (1857–1932), was performed by using a magnet, just like the very first cure obtained by Mesmer a century earlier.

At Salpêtrière, Charcot was studying what he called *grand*

hypnotisme (deep hypnotism), which implied loss of consciousness. In the meantime, at Nancy, the doctors were obtaining results from subjects often so uninfluenced that they wondered whether they had been asleep or not because they could remember everything about the consultation. This state was termed *petit hypnotisme* (light hypnotism).

Both levels—and both schools—should have been complementary, but there was no resemblance between the two schools. Even without real collaboration, however, their combined efforts earned universal renown. The Nancy school was based on psychology and verbal suggestion, while the Salpêtrière school neglected the mental state and concerned itself only with examining sensitivity and the reflexes, which, it was believed, one could affect by material means—by magnets, as we have seen, and by the application of various metal plates.

The use of metal plates was developed in 1876 by Dr. Burcq. He had noticed that a copper door knob had made one of his patients pass into a cataleptic state. When the patient recovered, the object was no longer effective. As he was interested in magnetism, Burcq then studied the action of copper on subjects that he was treating in several clinics and observed that they were sensitive to this metal. Dismissed by the hospital because of his belief in magnetism, he decided to write to Claude Bernard, president of the Biological Society. This great physiologist recommended that the question be looked into. Experiments were performed at Salpêtrière. The hysterical patients there were insensitive to copper plates that were placed on their arms but did appear sensitive to gold plates. Vulpian (1826–1887), a physiologist and a member of the Academy of Sciences, came as a skeptical observer but went away convinced. "All the causes of error were eliminated . . . all the reports of the Biological Society are unanimous on this point. These details illustrate the strict methods of observation that must be used in the examination of scientific facts." This was the serious conclusion reached by Dr. Faveau de Courmelles, vice-president of the 1889 International Magnetic Congress in his book entitled *L'Hypnotisme.*

It was following this research that Charcot and his disciples decided to carry out large-scale experimentation.

The quarrel between the animists and the fluidists, with the psychologists from Nancy on the one side and the Salpêtrière magnetizers on the other, was close to being revived. But Bernheim in Nancy did not want to get involved in a dispute on these grounds. His friend Liébeault was not entirely convinced that the magnetic-fluid theory could be completely discredited because he had obtained results from some babies, where there could have been no question of psychological influence. Furthermore, the Salpêtrière school had obtained many positive results. Nevertheless, Bernheim had the treatment of thousands of patients chosen at random from Nancy as his evidence, and he proved that Charcot, whose observations were based on only a handful of specially chosen hysterical patients, was practicing only a "cultivated hypnotism."

Another institution that added to the debate among hypnotizers was the School of Charity. This Parisian school, which for a time rivaled the Salpêtrière school, had as its leader Dr. Luys (1828–1895), a member of the Academy of Medicine. As a doctor at Salpêtrière, he had been a member of the committee appointed to examine Burcq's "discovery" concerning the influence of metals. Impressed by this theory, Luys admitted the action of physical agents, even from a distance. He also admitted the possibility of influencing a hypnotized subject by placing medication or other substances in a sealed tube on the subject's neck or even by simply bringing it near the subject. The reactions varied according to the product being used. For example, Luys placed colored glass balls in the hands of his sleeping patients and these would produce various emotions depending on the color. Luys was the first to use a revolving mirror to induce hypnosis. In 1888, Dujardin-Beaumetz reported to the Academy of Medicine that Luys' experiments were conducted so carelessly as to rob them of all value.

THE END IN SIGHT

The victory of the Nancy school was no longer in doubt after the death of Charcot. But his death was disastrous nevertheless. At Nancy, where all diseases were treated, hypnotism was not sufficiently organized to form a solid branch of the medical arts. At Paris very few treatments were undertaken—only ex-

Hippolyte Bernheim
(1827-1919)—*Holzapfel*

periments. When Charcot died, his associates stopped their experimentation. Because it lacked an established sphere of study, hypnotism gradually sank into obscurity and then into oblivion. There was no one in France with the stature necessary to put it back on the right path. One man perhaps might have been able to prevent this collapse.

Like Mesmer, Sigmund Freud also studied at Salpêtrière and Nancy. He wrote the preface for the German translation of Bernheim's book. Freud used hypnotism in the treatment of neuroses, but then stopped it because he did not find it accurate enough. A personal experiment made him fear that the hypnotist could find himself open to an effusive attachment on the part of the subject. So he perfected a very different method of psychic exploration. We all know the result of this. Psychoanalysis captivated the public because of the importance it placed on sexuality and the interpretation of dreams, two topics that will always be of interest to man.

With the decline of the two schools at Nancy and Salpêtrière, whose prestige was such that every hypnotist of that period had two homelands, his own and France, the French torch was dimmed. When the disciples of Charcot, Bernheim, and the School of Charity lost their faith, the reaction was as sudden as their hopes and ambitions had been excessive. The number of publications on hypnotism very rapidly fell from two or three thousand a year to a few dozen, and in 1910 the *Revue de l'hypnotisme* ("Journal of Hypnotism"), mouthpiece for the ideas of Dr. Edgar Berillon since 1897, changed its name to *Revue de psychologie appliquée* ("Journal of Applied Psychology").

After Charcot's death, his disciples oriented themselves differently and made excellent use of the knowledge acquired at Salpêtrière. One of these disciples was Pierre Janet (1859–1947), teacher, doctor of literature, and head of the pathological psychology laboratory. He had completed his medical studies in 1893 and became chairman of the department of experimental psychology at the Collège de France ten years later. Recognized as one of the masters of psychopathology and contemporary philosophy, he never repudiated his early work under Charcot. Even at the end of his career, he set aside an important place for hypnotism in his large work on psychological medications. This was noteworthy at a time when almost everyone in France was classifying hypnotism as one of the hoaxes of occultism. On the other hand, Babinski, head of Charcot's clinic and the virtuoso of the transference experiments with a large magnet, changed his mind, very quickly accepting the theory of "suggestibility." He gave the Greek name "pithiatism" (curable by suggestion) to the phenomenon that had previously been the highlight of the Salpêtrière school.

A Swiss from Berne, Dubois, then offered the theory that persuasion, which calls on reason, bears the stamp of idealism, whereas suggestion does not, since suggestion is directed at the subject's automatic tendencies. Bernheim, the leader of the Nancy school, accepted this point of view. So, a new stage was reached. Hypnotism had yielded to suggestion, which, in turn, was now giving way to persuasion. The gradual process was becoming more and more reassuring, but it was tending toward zero. Soon this harmless, insignificant field of knowledge was no longer of interest. From then on, it was finished in France. Hypnotism was not practiced any more, or only rarely.

Of course, it is easy to find evidence that there were still numerous hypnotists during World War I, but they were experimenting more often than they were providing treatment. Consequently, after the war "enlightened" men imposed their views and authoritatively classified hypnotism as charlatanic practice and a fake. According to them, the hypnotists and the hypnotized subjects were involved in a constant effort to get the better of each other, while at the same time both were trying to fool themselves.

STARTING AGAIN FROM SCRATCH

Hypnotism was going out of style in the rest of the world, too. Other easier and more promising therapies took its place. First, Christian Science (a religion that teaches that diseases can be cured by spiritual means), then psychoanalysis conquered the United States. The United States treated hypnotism with more reserve than did France, but like Freud, did not deny its existence. It remained a method of investigation to which men resorted in order to explore the automatic and, on occasion, obscure and unfathomable aspects of human behavior.

The situation was the same in England, Germany, Holland, Switzerland, and Denmark. And likewise in Russia, where one of the greatest physiologists of all time, Ivan Pavlov (1849–1936), gave a great deal of consideration to hypnosis in his famous study on conditioned reflexes. World War II precipitated events. Military psychiatrists were glad to use hypnotism to accelerate the treatment of certain neuroses. Rid of the errors stemming from somnambulism and magnetism when they had been used experimentally on hysterical patients, and back in vogue now on the stage, the practice of hypnotism led to incontestable applications in dentistry, obstetrics, and the treatment of psychoneuroses, especially in the United States and Russia. In England, Parliament passed an act in 1955 forbidding stage hypnotists to give potentially dangerous demonstrations of a medication whose significance was still not really known but which had already shown beneficial applications.

At about the same time, hypnotism made its way back to France. Groups were formed, and there were some conferences. The press proceeded to show that, even though the subject was still a perplexing one, disparagement was no longer appropriate and that public opinion was recognizing both hypnotism as a fact and hypnology as a science.

PART II

THE PHENOMENON OF HYPNOSIS

CHAPTER IV

What Is Hypnosis?

IN order to describe the properties of a body or an object, we must first indicate, as precisely and simply as possible, the exact nature of the body or object in question. This precaution is even more necessary when describing an action, because an action has neither the unity nor the materiality of an object.

Unfortunately, it is not always easy to find an accurate definition, and we regret that we cannot provide an exact definition of hypnotism. For half a century men were reasonably satisfied with the definition, "artificially provoked sleep." But then, when they realized that the subjects were not really asleep and therefore the definition was both false and dangerous, no one was willing to risk altering it. The more competent the writers, the more cautious they were, which is understandable, as hypnosis was revealing itself to be more and more complex and less and less explainable.

"By observing, we will eventually understand it," was the belief of some. "We have established phenomena proving its existence—that is the main thing," said Charcot's disciples. But then someone retorted, "You are not practicing hypnotism, you are merely training hysterical patients!" And Charcot's disciples had to admit that this was true. Although their work was very valuable for the study of neuroses, they had gone beyond the bounds of their intended sphere of study and beyond the framework of their definition, however vague that definition may have been.

Hypnosis. Hypnotism. Which is the correct word? "Whichever you wish," was Dr. R. Chertok's reply in his excellent treatise published in 1959. "Both can be used indifferently." And this is an authoritative opinion, if ever there was one. Yet Dr. Chertok must have had a preference for "hypnosis," since he chose this as the title of his book.

We shall adopt it too. As a rule, there is a general tendency to prefer "hypnosis." The reason we have avoided using it until now is that we wished to emphasize the change in periods. "Hypnosis" seems preferable because it includes both the state into which the patient is put and the methods used to put him into it.

Braid, after only four years, already regretted having chosen the word "hypnotism." (In actual fact, he did not invent the word, because it had already appeared, though was not used, in the catalogue of words drawn up by Hénin de Cuvilliers in 1820.) Braid had been very quick to note that the subjects who were "sleeping" were a minority, one out of ten at the most. On the other hand, he observed that the subjects who were influenced beneficially while asked only to concentrate their thoughts were much more numerous.

By various methods—verbal suggestions or physical sensations—Braid made his patients concentrate their thoughts on one part or one function of their body. This concentration of the entire brain on one single idea produced excellent results without the subjects having to pass into a state resembling sleep. So, in 1847, Braid proposed a new terminology, based on the term "monoideism," which designated the condition resulting from the mind being possessed by one dominant idea.

This fresh terminology, which he was unable to impose, did not fully satisfy him either. He adopted a third point of view before his death in 1860. The state he had described as hypnotic, then as monoideistic, then seemed to him to appear rather like a state of "double consciousness." Thus even the father of hypnotism feared that the name he had chosen was ambiguous and never stopped searching for the term that could most accurately be applied to the phenomena of "hypnotism."

In trying to define hypnosis, we can only advance step by step. We have already pointed out that Braid eventually observed that hypnotism was not dependent on the action of a fluid. Today this is an established fact, but it is worthwhile coming back to it.

No serious hypnotist today would invoke the existence or even the influence of this fluid. Yet Mesmer believed in it, as did Esdaile, Elliotson, and many others after them. Charcot, Luys, Babinski, and the Salpêtrière and Charity schools believed in the effectiveness of magnets. Millions of people still believe in the efficacy of the magnetizer's touching and stroking.

IT IS NOT HYSTERIA

Hysteria is another disturbing phenomenon that was often associated with hypnosis. But today it is no longer considered as a definition for hypnosis. In Charcot's clinics the theory that hypnotism and hysteria were identical was a dogma. "It is only in the hypnotism of hysterical patients, in that form described by Messrs. Charcot and Richer under the name of *grand hypnotisme* [deep hypnotism], that we have discovered physical phenomena imprinting a special character on their sleep." The authors of this comment, Binet and Feré, added that, even though it could be proved that no person is absolutely immune to hypnotism, hypnotic phenomena consisted of a regular functional disorder of the organism that went hand in hand with hysteria.

Bernheim and the Nancy school attacked this Salpêtrière theory, gallantly maintaining that there was no relation between hypnotism and hysteria. In the heat of the discussion, Bernheim went too far, that is certain. Even today, knowing that if the hypnotist is patient enough it is possible to lead a normal subject into the deepest levels of hypnosis, we do admit that hysterical patients make the best subjects, and possibly the only perfect subjects for certain demonstrations that do not necessarily illustrate the curative properties of hypnosis.

Babinski tried to prove that hysteria was the diseased manifestation of hypnosis. And so he found it convenient to combine the two under the common designation "pithiatism." (Hysteria, derived from the Greek, *hystera,* meaning "womb," was formerly thought to be a protestation of the unsatisfied female organism. The English anatomist Thomas Willis (1622–1675) was the first to see the involvement of the nervous system.) Even when Babinski had given up trying to make one subject's spasm pass to another subject, or to make a normal patient's disease pass to a hysterical patient by means of a large-caliber magnet, he still claimed that hysteria and hypnotism were identical.

"Hypnotism is a psychic state causing the subject in this state to be susceptible to the suggestion of others. It is a state manifested by phenomena which are instigated by suggestions, which can be made to disappear by suggestions and which are identical to hysterical phenomena." So, according to Babinski, the disappearance of a hysterical phenomenon, for example, paralysis of the arm, is explained by the hypnotic induction technique. Using this method, the doctor would prove to the patient that he could make various other paralyses appear and disappear at will, so that in this way the paralysis of the arm, theoretically incurable, could also disappear as well.

Thanks to references like this, hypnosis became a sort of disease: the involuntary revelation of artificial symptoms of neuroses. And so no one wanted to admit that he was hypnotizable, with the result that most of the experiments failed because the patients were unreasonably hostile.

Considering anyone who is hypnotizable as hysterical seems all the more unfounded when today it is acknowledged that any normal person can be influenced and that only the mentally deficient—the dull, the stupid, or the infantile—are difficult to influence.

IT IS NOT SLEEP

This fact can never be emphasized too much: *it is only in a very advanced stage that hypnosis becomes a state of sleep involving loss of consciousness.*

It is very easy to be hypnotized and to accept suggestions while consciously paying attention to the hypnotist and his orders throughout the entire sitting. Occasionally subjects even believe that they have carried out his orders of their own free will so as not to oppose him. This does not matter, since often it is all that is required. Because the subject has not lost consciousness (as is the case in real sleep), he concludes that he has not slept (which is true) and therefore that he has not been influenced (which is not true). A state of relative passivity can develop very early and this state does not resemble sleep; yet it can produce results, as Liébeault showed.

This progression toward a passive state bears a name when it involves the nervous system: *inhibition*. Any decrease or suppression of nervous activity through inhibition favors hypnosis, so the hypnotist therefore tries to make the subject concentrate his attention in a limited field. Furthermore, this procedure will only be successful if the subject has not fallen into a normal sleep. If the subject should actually fall asleep, he must be awakened and led back into a hypnotic sleep. So, in order to prevent the subject from falling asleep through boredom or indifference, the hypnotist must constantly monopolize the patient's attention, by speaking to him or from time to time asking him to perform a certain activity, specially chosen because of its automatic nature.

As we have realized, this cannot be termed sleeping. For those who still have doubts about this, there is various scientific evidence to confirm it. The respiration and cardiac rhythm of the hypnotized subject, for instance, are much closer to those of a waking state than those of a sleeping state. The basal metabolism rate, which is less in sleep, is not affected under hypnosis. Some reflexes, such as those caused by taps on the knee or ankle, which are very reduced or suppressed during sleep, persist in the hypnotized subject.

IT IS NOT A PARALYSIS

After disposing of magnetic fluid, hysteria, and sleep, what else can we eliminate from the definition? Some of Braid's disciples believed that the state of hypnosis was caused by a sort of spasm, similar to the puckering of the face that had been produced in Mrs. Braid by her fixed gazing at the lid of a sugar bowl. According to their theory, this spasm occurred when the circulation of the blood in the brain became reduced, thus causing cerebral ischemia and diminished psychic activity. But this theory of reduced cerebral circulation as a basis for hypnosis was subsequently rejected. Pierre Janet adequately summed it up:

> It is useless to try and explain hypnosis by theories concerning the physiological symptoms of hypnotism, or to define hypnosis as cerebral congestion, cerebral ischemia, a paralysis or excitation of certain areas of the brain, or dissociations of certain cerebral centers. Unfortunately, these theories are no more valid than the magnetizers' dreams about a "nervous fluid" which was directed through space onto the individuals whom they wished to influence.

Janet knew what he was talking about. He had written reports disclaiming attempts to hypnotize from a distance, and in comparison with these, Berna's claims of being able to magnetize his girlfriend through a door are mere diversions. In any case, it has been proved that hypnosis is caused neither by cerebral ischemia nor by cerebral congestion. As we shall see, there are violent and mechanical methods of hypnotizing a subject by abruptly stopping the flow of blood to the cerebrum. But even if these dangerous procedures do precipitate the process, they do not change the nature of it and it seems that we can eliminate any physical modifications of the state of the brain from the definition.

Can we go further? Of course, because enlightened suggestions are never lacking.

According to Dr. Aimé Albert (who waited until the last page of his excellent treatise to discuss the tricky problem of the definition), hypnotism "becomes the scientific utilization of words, considered as a medication, on a subject prepared to receive them, by methods adapted to each individual case." The importance accorded here to the spoken word is completely justified. Albert speaks admirably about it, believing that "language is what makes the human condition," and pointing out the magic way in which certain words, such as "cure," "sleep," "rejuvenate," are sufficient to place the seeds of a renewal in the patient's mind and give him a breath of hope.

It is through the spoken word that the hypnotist exercises his action, and this is what will guide the subject toward a possible cure. So Albert's definition expresses very well the role hypnotism plays in healing in his book *L'Hypnotisme dans la médecine* ("Hypnotism in Medicine"). But this definition restricts the field of hypnosis too much because it is concerned only with hypnotic suggestion as described by Pavlov. By doing this, Albert neglects the results that were occasionally obtained even before the intervention of the spoken word.

In addition to atmosphere, environment, and contagion, other factors, such as thermal stimulation (warm surroundings), tactile stimulation (light stroking), visual stimulation (dazzlement, ocular spasms), and auditory stimulation (metronome, monotonous noise), can also be used to induce a hypnotic trance, thus making words unnecessary. The spoken word completes the procedure, ensures the result, and above all helps the hypnotist to monopolize the subject's attention. It does indeed finish off the procedure, but the other factors are a definite part of hypnotism too.

Yet one could reply that it is through the spoken word that suggestion is conveyed. Naturally, but once again, this is not the only method. Imitation and contagion can be just as effective as verbal suggestion. Taking these aspects into consideration Dr. A. A. Mason gives us a new definition: "Hypnosis is a temporary state of modified attention which is characterized by increased suggestibility."

Eighty years ago Bernheim also saw increased suggestibility as the only difference between hypnosis and the normal waking state. And he eloquently defended suggestion, that instrument of persuasion whose effects he found everywhere. Freud deplored the "tyranny" of suggestibility as a human weakness unfortunately found in all circumstances.

And therein lies the difficulty. Suggestibility is a universal fault able easily to be exploited. Hence it is not an exclusive characteristic of the hypnotic state. Suggestibility does not imply a particular state. It is a state of mind. It is the state of a lover wildly overcome with emotion. It is Othello's state of blind jealousy. In both these states, the subjects believe everything and accept all suggestions. Yet they are not in a hypnotic state, or everything would be hypnosis.

Mason's definition is preferable to Bernheim's, because it emphasizes the subject's modified attention, but like Albert's definition, it takes other hypnotic agents into account only incidentally.

CONCERNING THE DANGER OF DEFINITIONS

Mason also wrote, "If it is absolutely necessary to define hypnosis, we could say that it is a certain psychological state reinforced by certain physiological processes. The final point, which is the hypnotic trance, varies like a cake, according to the proportions of the various ingredients."

A psychological state reinforced by physiological processes, and which results in a trance—a highly variable trance as we already know, since it can be imperceptible—this covers a large area of the field in question. And, in particular, this definition includes animal hypnosis, which not all schools find comparable to the hypnosis of man but which very few consider negligible. However, the beginning of the definition appears rather vague. Since an extremely marked trance is not compulsory (otherwise we would run the risk of being as obstinate as the Salpêtrière school), there is no lack of psychological states that reinforce and aggravate a physiological process, thus answering the above description but nevertheless having nothing to do with hypnosis.

Anger, for example, is a psychological state that is reinforced by physiological processes because congestion makes the face of a plethoric person turn purple and his fury can cause him to cough and choke. Likewise, a soldier's panic on the battlefield is a psychological state reinforced by physiological processes. Charlet portrayed soldiers nailed to the spot as a result of the physiological effects of their psychological state—there was nothing hypnotic about it.

So, once more, we see that greater accuracy of definition is needed.

A WORKING THEORY

When the specialists seem cautious, it is natural that the writers discussing the works of the scientists should also show discretion. However, whereas the scientist is criticized for the slightest discrepancy, the commentator is excused and so, under these circumstances, it is almost his duty to assume the risk that is closed to the scientist. It is in this spirit, to serve as a simple working theory for the publication of this work and to allow for a better understanding of the topic, that we propose provisionally the following definition of hypnosis, for lack of a better one:

Hypnosis is a particular state of the nervous system in which the organized inhibition of certain areas permits unaccustomed action. The trance can constitute one of its characteristics. Suggestibility can be one of its elements, and perhaps also conditioned reflexes.

But by viewing the facts too narrowly, and by trying to give too precise a definition, we find that this definition can be applied only to one particular technique. Therefore, until the ideal definition is found, we shall let everyone be responsible for making his own combination of the factors constituting a definition of hypnosis.

One final remark about the word "inhibition." We had first written "passivity," but then we remembered Pavlov's terminology: "Sleep and inhibition—they are one and the same thing. While inhibition is a concentrated phenomenon, hypnosis and sleep are an inhibition which is propagated to more or less vast areas."

Obviously the similarity between hypnosis and sleep is by no means complete, but the term "inhibition" in our definition does introduce the notion of suppression comparable to sleep, which was considered the essential characteristic of hypnosis for a very long time. It only became bothersome because of the ambiguity.

In our opinion, the term "inhibition" does not cause any confusion, and we shall readily use it because, according to Pavlov, excitation and inhibition control all the acts of our conscious and unconscious lives. By reflecting this balance, the definition obtains a certain harmony. However, it is only an uncertain attempt which can be improved upon, and it is with humility that we propose it.

CHAPTER V

Hypnosis in Animals

BY excluding animals arbitrarily and limiting the problem of hypnosis to man, we are deprived of certain interesting information. While Charcot was obtaining disconcerting results from his hysterical patients, Charles Richet (1850–1935, Nobel Prize winner in 1913), a young man with a great future and a precursor in many fields, was suggesting in the *Journal de l'anatomie et de la physiologie* ("Journal of Anatomy and Physiology") that "in order to judge the question of simulation, nothing could be simpler than to experiment on creatures that are unable to put on an 'act,'" and therefore to experiment on animals.

We are justified in feeling skeptical about the inability of animals to simulate. When a young blackbird that cannot yet fly has fallen out of its nest and a cat is creeping up on it, the parent birds have been seen to feign a broken wing and limp along right under the cat's very nose to distract its attention away from the young bird. The partridge does likewise to lure a dog away from its brood. And there are many similar examples.

Experimentation on animals is not new. In fact, animal hypnosis was being studied even before Mesmer's discoveries. In 1646, in a book entitled *Ars magna lucis et umbrae,* the Jesuit scientist Athanasius Kircher described what he called "a marvelous experiment." The head of a chicken was pressed lightly to the ground and a line traced with chalk straight in front of its beak; the chicken was held in this uncomfortable position for a few moments. The animal gradually became still. Then it could be untied, and it would not move even when the experimenters tried to bring it out of its cataleptic state. A similar demonstration had been described a few years earlier by Schwenter in *Deliciae physico-mathematicae* (1636). Schwenter had calmed a chicken by balancing a wood shaving, folded in half, on the bird's beak.

Such experiments were easily and often performed. People everywhere were trying to see who could put the widest variety of animals into this "pseudosleep." In the mid-nineteenth century in Germany, traveling shows went from town to town with miniature circuses made up of sparrows, rabbits, frogs, snakes, pigeons, salamanders, and crayfish. These animals were gradually "petrified" by passes made from the head to the tail.

The question was studied by scientific men, whose experiments were, of course, even more impressive than the variety-show performances. Czermak (1828–1873) succeeded in making a chicken become rigidly immobile without tying its legs together. Preyer (1841–1897), professor of biology at the universities of Jena, Berlin, and Wiesbaden, paralyzed a triton simply by pinching its tail. Czermak attributed this pseudosleep both to fixed gazing and to the compression of certain nerves and ganglions when the operator exerted pressure on certain parts of the animal's body. Preyer, however, attributed it to fright. According to Preyer, two different states could be distinguished. The first was a hypnotic stupor obtained by gentle, prolonged excitation. The second state was cataleptic and instantaneous, resulting from fear; certain elements of fright brought about inner inhibitions in the nervous system as well as a paralysis of the muscles. This new theory that Preyer advanced was further supported by the frequently perceived signs of anxiety and fear in the animals: trembling, noisy breathing, increased heartbeat, fixed gaze, and vigorous peristalsis (with defecation).

Preyer was invited to read a paper at Cambridge, during which he showed how small animals such as rats and guinea pigs could instantly become stiff and immobile in the most varied and unusual positions. He even made a frog remain immobile on a rope for eighty hours. It would have mummified there, passing from catalepsy to stupor to a hypnotic coma, if it had not been awakened by means of a few drops of boric acid. At about the same period, Darwin, who had witnessed some experi-

The Jesuit scientist Athanasius Kircher puts a chicken in a cataleptic state—*Holzapfel*

ments in animal hypnosis, was also ascribing the rigidity of small birds to the effects of fright. Nevertheless Preyer considered that, all in all, the problem of animal hypnosis had not been approached scientifically. After Preyer, explorations were made in many directions.

Verworn (1861–1921), an eminent scientist, gained notoriety by investigating the automatism and origin of certain postural reflexes, such as the "clasping reflex" of frogs and toads during mating. He found that even when the male was burned or decapitated, he did not release the female but maintained his hold. In the case of the clasping reflex, the animal is rigid, as in a cataleptic state. Furthermore, the creature is completely dominated by its sexual instincts, which makes us think of Braid's monoideism—the condition resulting from the mind being possessed by one dominant idea. All the same, the relation to human hypnosis is remote.

If we have certain doubts about these controlled manifestations of animal hypnosis, what can we say about uncontrolled examples of it? In 1894, Émile Mesnet of the Academy of Medicine drew up a list of examples of fascination that could be observed in both animals and humans. Among his examples were the fascination of a sparrow in a field paralyzed by a hovering hawk, and the snake's fascination over a frog. And this can be extended to all birds that on sensing danger "try to flee but flap their wings in vain, and uttering cries, give themselves up in sacrifice."

We suspect that none of this has been proved scientifically. The snake's reputation as a hypnotist has stemmed from the fact that its eyelids, which are joined together, are transparent and cover the eye like a sort of watch crystal. As the ocular ball is not very mobile, there results a fixed gaze which has been misnamed fascinating. As far as fascination in humans is concerned, we shall refer to it again in the study of methods of inducing hypnosis. Originally it was introduced by Faria, who used both the spoken word and fixed gazing as part of his procedure.

A PETRIFIED ZOO

This naturalist lore was hardly promising, and in fact very little had been learned since LaFontaine had mesmerized a lion in the London zoo or since the great Frenchman J.-H. Fabre (1823–1915) had transformed a whole flock of turkeys into rigid, almost cadaver-like recumbent figures. He put the head of each turkey suddenly under its wing, spun the bird around, and immediately it became drowsy.

This experiment has worked successfully on many types of birds. In the Caux region of France farmers force hens to sit on eggs that are not their own. When the hen begins to brood, the farmer's wife takes it and places its head under one wing, shakes it a few times, and then places the hen in the nest that has been prepared for it. On waking the hen stays there.

These experiments may seem questionable, but they are possible because of the way in which the bird's neck, when bent around, brings the head toward the center of gravity. This centrifugal movement causes very complex phenomena to occur in the animal, the simplest of which is inversely related to the "flight blindness" of aviators. This loss of vision when the pilot is seated in his normal position occurs after fast positive acceleration. The visual disorders preceding loss of consciousness of the pilot are caused by purely mechanical reasons. The effects of the weight of the liquid filling the eyeball are added to those of the accelerated blood flow.

Most birds can be put to sleep in some way. A skillful Hungarian hypnotizer named Volgyesi exercised his power over all the animals in the Budapest zoo. Canaries, eagle owls, peacocks, and storks were all excited and then subdued by him. And the untiring Nimrod rarely failed to have his photo taken with the stiffened victim at his feet. Moreover, he did not limit himself to birds. He succeeded in hypnotizing a lion by fixation of the eyes; a mandrill, which he first put on its back, then paralyzed with his gaze; and a fox, by making passes. There are photographs attesting to all these feats. The photo of the lion is the least convincing. Volgyesi did not make it lie down, but he himself straddled it, which isn't terribly impressive.

As a result of his experiments, however, and the hypnotizing of some twenty-seven thousand humans, Volgyesi reached the conclusion that hypnosis disconnected certain cerebral centers by blood congestion. This opinion was rejected by Pierre Janet a long time ago, as we have already seen. Volgyesi also put forward other curious hypotheses. Even though his investigations were not very orthodox and his experiments lacked scientific precision, we can at least concede to this Hungarian virtuoso that numerically he went further than any of Kircher's other rivals. After Volgyesi there were hardly any animals left to hypnotize!

CONDITIONED REFLEXES

Ivan Petrovitch Pavlov (1849–1936) devoted himself almost exclusively to observing dogs, and his incontestable, concise experimentation proceeded to upset everything. As a result of his research, it was believed that animal hypnosis was far from being a marginal experimental field, that it could become vital, and that, in the light of phenomena observed in dogs, men would at last be able to understand what occurred in human hypnosis.

Pavlov, whose name will always be linked in the history of science with conditioned reflexes, was not a psychiatrist, a psychologist, or a neurologist. Neither was he a hypnotist. He was a physiologist.

In the beginning, his research did not involve hypnosis. He studied higher nervous activity and the functioning of the cerebral hemispheres, which in man are composed of billions of cells. He obtained confirmation that man's psychic life is a specific activity of the cerebral hemispheres. Thanks to his experiments performed on animals, we now know that when certain areas of the cerebrum are destroyed or impaired, some functions become impossible. For example, in man the destruction of half the cerebral cortex causes only slight effects, but ablation of both temporal lobes produces very important changes.

When faced with the study of the brain, the positive knowledge we have is only a beginning and is of a general nature. We know that a certain defect in the senses is caused by an impairment in a specific area. Occasionally the lesion can be localized, but the information is insignificant. The billions of brain cells that we possess remain a mystery to us.

Ivan Petrovitch Pavlov
(1849-1936)—*Corson*

Reflexes are what we still know best in this vast field. By considering the activity of animals as automatic, René Descartes believed that their acts were reflexes and that the organism's entire activity was a response provoked by an outside agent. Experiments were made with this orientation to investigate how responses to external stimuli are regulated. By progressing step by step, we have been able to determine which centers control certain reflexes. This was possible so long as the reflex in question occurred in that part of the nervous system controlling a very obvious action, such as balance, standing upright, or walking.

PAVLOV'S EXPERIMENT

By the beginning of the twentieth century, the study of animal reflexes concentrated on the cerebral hemispheres. Pavlov resolved to continue this study in a strictly objective way. He believed that knowing the reason for reflexes would allow us to know the reason for instincts, which he considered as combinations and series of reflexes. Pavlov's experiment has often been described. A bell was sounded every time a dog was given its food. After this had been repeated several times, the dog began to salivate as soon as it heard the tone. From then on, the tone was able to control the animal's alimentary reflex. This reflex, which disappeared after the dog's hemispheres had been ablated, had been formed (conditioned) and occurred only under certain circumstances (it was conditional). It should be emphasized that the conditioned reflex occurs in the cerebral hemispheres, in that part of the cerebrum that contributes the most to man's intellectual activity.

Pavlov pursued these investigations for almost half a century, and they constitute an enormous contribution to all the sciences because the results he obtained can be control-checked and cross-checked with similar investigations.

Like Freud's discoveries in psychology, Pavlov's aroused universal interest. Social groups, nations, and even whole blocs of nations made it a matter of doctrine either to admit them or reject them.

PAVLOV ENCOUNTERS HYPNOSIS WITHOUT LOOKING FOR IT

Pavlov, who was concerned only with the functioning of the cerebral hemispheres, encountered hypnosis without looking for it. He noticed that his dogs that had been partially decerebrated occasionally showed only delayed reactions or reactions opposite to those they should have displayed. They would salivate but would not eat the food. Pavlov considered this a manifestation of inhibition and a step toward sleep. Under certain conditions, he succeeded in producing this artificially provoked sleep in his dogs, which at that time was the characteristic element of hypnosis.

From then on, he became interested in hypnosis and, extending his research into a new direction, succeeded in provoking in some of his dogs another phenomenon, namely hysteria, which was then generally associated with the hypnotic state. When he confused his dogs with incoherent or contradictory signals, the animals would have violent nervous crises. He also obtained other phenomena associated with hypnosis, and came to the conclusion that hypnosis and sleep were one and the same thing, with hypnosis being a partial sleep during which part of the cerebral hemispheres remained alert. We have already remarked that, in man, at any rate, the physiological characteristics of hypnosis and sleep are very different. However, Pavlov admitted that the analogies he had observed between sleep and hypnosis were not a complete explanation for all animal hypnosis. He made a distinction between the nervous crises provoked in his dogs and the cataleptic states obtained in the whole Noah's ark of Kircher's successors. For Pavlov, the stiffness of "hypnotized" animals constituted a defense reaction: the animal was feigning death. Incapable of struggling or fleeing, it remained still so as to attract the least amount of attention possible, because everything that moves is quickly noticed.

J.-H. Fabre held a similar view. In addition to the turkeys he had put to sleep, he had also paralyzed beetles and spiders with fear. He too believed that this artificial sleep in animals could provide a point of departure in the study of hypnosis.

Those holding this belief are no doubt not so numerous as they once were. Catalepsy in itself does not prove anything. At the end of the last century Verworn showed that this rigidity in animals was the result of an incapability to move, a sort of stupor, which, however, did not extend to all their functions. For example, some of the animals, while transfixed, followed the operator with their eyes.

This partial stupor can also be observed in man. Claudius Vincent mentioned it in his study of hysteria in subjects afflicted with violent shock on the battlefield. The individual is stupefied, unable to gesticulate, and occasionally has urinary incontinence. But, he concluded, the "manifestations of this emotional crisis do not vary from individual to individual as an attack of hysteria does." Nor does it have anything in common with hypnotic catalepsy in human beings, which occurs in a completely opposite way to what Verworn observed in some animals. In humans, catalepsy of the eyes, or fixed gazing, is obtained very quickly at the beginning of a slight hypnotic trance, whereas complete catalepsy of the limbs comes later, at the threshold of a deep trance. So there is no similarity with animals, where rigidity occurs immediately.

However, it is not possible to write, like some authors who try to explain everything by mechanics, that the animal stupor results from a series of reflexes, as described for example by Sganarelle, who enumerated these reflexes in *Le Médecin malgré lui* ("The Doctor in Spite of Himself"). In the last century reasoning of this type was used to explain that woodchucks hibernated as the result of a series of reflexes set off by cold weather. On the strength of this, Charcot tried to find a contrary Madagascar mouse that would "hibernate" to get away from the heat!

POSTHYPNOTIC SUGGESTION

Weitzenhofer, an American, claimed that animals have never been able to be influenced by posthypnotic suggestions. Was he pointing out the difference between human hypnosis and animal hypnosis, or was he making a distinction between training and hypnosis? For this is like suggesting that an animal has never been able to learn how to conjugate the future tense of a verb.

In human hypnosis there is nothing extraordinary about posthypnotic suggestion—and by this we mean the suggestion of an act to be performed by the subject after he has awakened. The suggestion can be executed in a slight trance. The words "When you wake up, you will do this at such and such a time . . ." obviously imply the idea of an act to be performed in the future. Furthermore, this is not a future time progressively led up to by a series of events, as is the case with conditioned reflexes, but a future connected with a particular piece of information unknown to the subject. The piece of information can be arbitrary, strange, or even stupid. It doesn't matter. The ensuing action will be carried out as though the information were a perfectly logical point of departure.

"When you hear this song, you will fall asleep," said a British hypnotist to one of his subjects. The subject interpreted the word "when" to mean "whenever." The tune was a popular one that was sung often, with the result that the subject fell asleep several times a day no matter what he was doing. So the hypnotist had to be called back in a hurry, as only he could erase the suggestion.

We must admit that some animals do have a notion of the future. There are some animals that store food. Many animals assure provisions for offspring they will never know. And most animals when they reach maturity act as though they know they have new responsibilities ahead of them. But this is instinctive knowledge, common to all species.

Implanting a particular idea for the future that goes against hereditary instincts seems all the more daring when this implantation, which occurs in the present, has not been formally proved. Pavlov declared that "in animals, there is basically an absolute reflex, that is to say, an excitation produced by the essential qualities of the object. A dog has to learn what is edible. A puppy brought up on milk will be indifferent to meat until someone makes him taste it."

The feeding reflex is innate—we could also say absolute. The reflex of eating meat is only an *acquired* reflex. Before wanting to eat meat, a dog must be *convinced* that meat interests him. Then, as in Pavlov's experiment, the reward of meat can be associated with all kinds of different rites, some of which might be unpleasant yet will nevertheless be accepted by the animal. But this conditioning is no doubt related more to training than to hypnosis.

"If we let a dog look at his regular food for days and weeks without giving it to him to eat, the sight of this food will finally cause him not to salivate any more." This statement by Pavlov is very significant. In other words, a conditioned reflex can be unlearned, but this takes time because it has been very firmly implanted.

A STRICTLY HUMAN DOMAIN

In human hypnosis, suggestions are accepted almost instantaneously. The operator merely has to suggest to the subject that an apple is tart or that a piece of bread is delicious for the suggestion to be accepted immediately. If he says, "There are poisonous mushrooms on this table," the subject turns away in disgust. But, if a moment later he tells the subject that the mushrooms have been replaced by delicious cakes, the subject will rush to eat them as soon as the invitation is extended. The first hypnotic suggestion has been erased like a pencil line. The hypnotized subject thought he was seeing mushrooms, then cakes.

For the animals that have learned to associate the sound of a bell with eating, however, it takes weeks to convince them that the bell may not be followed by food or that the food in front of them is not for them. This is because the animal has neither the faculty of illusion that makes it see what is not there, nor the imagination necessary to comprehend departures from what it considers the normal order, which it has learned from experience.

Working through the regular channels of the brain and the senses, we do not seem to be able to suggest to a dog an image different from food, which is the hoped-for result of all the bizarre and apparently incoherent phenomena that his master submits him to. A light doubles the intensity of the sound . . . a sound precedes the light . . . a scratching of the thigh occurs at the same time as the sound. One noise assures him there will be food to eat, another noise contradicts it. In this jumble of signals and sensations, it is remarkable that the dog does succeed in working out the signals meaning food and as a consequence salivates. These various sounds and images show, therefore, that the animal is capable of discriminating. It is fascinating to try and determine the centers and methods responsible for this—a study to which Pavlov devoted his whole life.

As far as the problem of animal hypnosis is concerned, it has scarcely progressed. It is still attributed to fright in smaller animals and to rhythmic stimulation in larger animals. Trainers still calm overexcited thoroughbreds with sedative stroking, and no scientific procedure has been found to replace the chants that the cowboys sing to put the longhorns to sleep when making the long climb up to Abilene.

CHAPTER VI

The Practical Significance of Hypnosis

IN animal hypnosis, we are confronted with phenomena provoking hypnosis in an unrefined state, for it is unlikely that intelligence is involved. The spoken word is only a signal, and suggestion and imagination scarcely play any role, while in human hypnosis these factors are essential. Furthermore, animal hypnosis can be induced only by mechanical measures, such as spinning the animal around, rolling it over onto its back, by passes or stroking, or other rather rudimentary measures. Intimidation, resulting from the omnipotence of the superior being through force, is the most "subtle" of these measures. And we can hardly claim that intimidation is subtle, even if it is caused by fixed gazing (whose action has not yet been clearly explained). Does fixed gazing produce a stupor that is caused by fear? Does it produce a somnolence caused by monotony? Or does it produce a stunned condition, as was the case with Pavlov's dogs, which were saturated with countless signals to which they must not respond? It does not matter. For the time being, we are trying to differentiate between human and animal hypnosis.

If animal and human hypnosis can legitimately be connected, we would have a fine example of this in the Haitian voodoo ceremony of sacrificial substitution described by W. B. Seabrook in *The Magic Island*. A young girl of marriageable age is kneeling before the altar with her hands on the ground, her breasts hanging down and her face close to a he-goat's muzzle. The goat stands very calmly. The virgin, with her hallucinated gaze, stares into the animal's blue eyes and bleats plaintively while the goat whimpers like a child. A leafy branch is brought close to their mouths, and the girl nibbles at it by pushing her lips forward like a ruminant. Suddenly the sacrifice is made. The priest's knife cuts the goat's throat and it collapses without uttering a sound. The virgin utters a shrill bleat, shudders, and falls unconscious.

Seabrook admitted that both the young girl, who was probably drugged, and the animal must have been under the influence of hypnosis. "We are surrounded by mysteries," he concluded, "and we think we can explain them by giving them a name!"

This parallelism between the two hypnoses—if there is more than one kind of hypnosis—does not allow us to claim that they are identical. If we disregard the animals put into a cataleptic state, hypnotists have not obtained very conclusive results from even the most intelligent animals. Dogs, for example, have shown outward symptoms of hypnosis without the practitioner having a subsequent hold over them, as he would through training. And hypnotists have obtained barely satisfactory results from animals with more marked individuality, such as monkeys and cats.

Thus, if some of the most intelligent animals resist hypnosis, we must ask ourselves why man is willing to undergo it. And this leads us to another question: What are the goals of hypnosis?

In addition to the information that it can provide about the functioning of our nervous system (in which case the subject is scarcely more than a guinea pig), hypnosis would be of no interest to the person willing to undergo it unless it could allow some action that would otherwise be impossible. And hypnosis does just this. We have seen that it has countless medical applications, such as in dentistry and obstetrics.

The stimulative power of hypnosis is widely recognized. The mind of the hypnotized subject becomes sharper and more receptive. Some subjects recall forgotten memories. Others learn better and have better and faster perception.

Although hypnosis accelerates certain intellectual processes, it can also favor relaxation. This quality has been given several names, the best known of which is "autogenic training," and it can have many salutary effects. Thus there are two reactions to hypnosis: stimulation or sedation. Moreover, this double action on the nervous system is not a characteristic of the nervous system. Like a pair of scales sensitive to the slightest impulse, it oscillates before making a given response. For example, there are some emotions that we cannot predict whether they will cause laughter or tears. Likewise, there are some hypnotic drugs that are designed to put the patient to sleep and that at first often cause the same sensations as fatigue, as seen by a sudden relaxation of the legs, followed by a feeling of general excitation, before the patient finally falls asleep.

OUR ORGANISM'S SPONTANEOUS ADAPTATION

Extraordinary metamorphoses can occur in animals. For example, if magnesium salts are sprayed on a rosebush that has been invaded by plant lice, a large number of these animals will be transformed and will acquire wings. We mention the case of these insects because it is permissible to conjecture about the existence of an ability in man to adapt, the center of which is situated beyond the thinking brain, in the unconscious. Some biologists believe that a similar process of metamorphosis could have been responsible for many of the exceptional phenomena of evolution.

Without trying to explain the biological past, we can ask ourselves if the unconscious does not already control some biological effects. We can also ask if the "effect of consciousness" in man does not primarily consist in acknowledging that his nonthinking centers are more important for everything concerning his animal life and therefore his health than the constantly meditating, higher levels of his nervous system.

It would then be in man's interests to go beyond his conscious thoughts and try to discipline or even influence his nonthinking centers; a number of ascetics in India have accomplished this. Thus, in addition to sharpening certain faculties and occasioning a salutary and curative relaxation, hypnosis could, because it acts on the lower layers of the cerebrum, very well provide us with a means of influencing our innermost being.

PART III

THE PRACTICE OF HYPNOSIS

CHAPTER VII

How to Provoke Hypnotic Sleep

THE hypnotist cannot dominate the subject immediately. He must first solicit the subject's cooperation and confidence before even beginning to hypnotize—a procedure that can be quite rapid or very long. Anyone who has faith in himself and believes in what he is undertaking can hypnotize, and everyone is hypnotizable. It is not necessary to have an iron will to influence a subject. It is even possible that it is the hypnotized person and not the hypnotist who has the more resolute and dominant character, for the subject's consent to the experiment is all that is required. This consent is essential, because only exceptionally weak-willed persons can be influenced against their will.

When there is no opposition, the percentage of nonhypnotizable subjects is very small, between 1 and 3 percent. The average number of failures among good practitioners is around 10 percent, but most subjects who are uninfluenced by one operator will succumb to another. Not everyone can be put into a deep trance, but almost everyone can be influenced. Idiots are no doubt the only people who are unquestionably stubborn. Temperamental and highly nervous people are difficult subjects, because they may find mental concentration difficult, but they will eventually succumb if they are patient. Intelligent people make the best subjects, provided they do not pride themselves on being both actors and spectators, for they must not attempt to analyze themselves or be too eager to succeed.

Even raving lunatics can be influenced, as was shown by Dr. Auguste Voisin at the end of the nineteenth century. The subject was held by two assistants and forced to look at a very bright light. After a while, sometimes as long as three hours, the exhausted lunatic would fall asleep. Today there is a whole range of drugs that calm the patient without violence and therefore make him more receptive.

THE HYPNOTIST NEEDS KNOWLEDGE, NOT A MYSTERIOUS POWER

The hypnotist's first duty is to make it clear to the patient that there is nothing about the procedure that implies the hypnotist has superiority over the subject. Nor is there any question of domination or a lasting dependence, as is sometimes feared. Except that the hypnotist possesses certain information that his subject does not, their roles could even be reversed. Formerly it was believed that a special mysterious power was necessary, but today we know that only a certain knowledge is required. Ignorance is very dangerous, especially when coupled with conceit. Extensive medical knowledge is necessary to use hypnosis usefully and without risks. But anyone with a basic grounding in the practice of it can find subjects who are particularly easily influenced with whom he will succeed.

The hypnotist must persuade his subject that he is a competent operator and, if possible, show him that he has a personality worthy of holding the subject's attention. This must be done unostentatiously, so as not to compromise the experiment. The hypnotist's efforts to dominate the subject should be limited to this.

The operator also needs to have a dignified manner as well as patience and understanding. It is imperative that he have well-cared-for, clean, soft hands that are not moist, even if he must use ointments to ensure this. However, in order to hypnotize, self-confidence is the only essential, basic requirement. The hypnotist must also feel the same desire to exercise an action that gave the pioneers of hypnotism the illusion that they possessed a special power. These pioneers were certainly right, even if they were mistaken about the nature of this power, which was not a magic power but a salutary one. A hypnotist can never know too much about his subject. And we know that the human intellect generally requires delicate handling.

CONVINCING THE SUBJECT

Some doctors of the old school devote their first meeting to getting to know their patient, letting him speak about his problems, and then explaining the treatment to him. This approach can provide the hypnotist with the opportunity to convince the subject of both his competence and the possible advantages of hypnosis. He can also give the subject an idea of how extensive the benefits of suggestibility can be; this is essential because, as a neophyte, the subject will probably have no idea of what to expect.

These preliminaries will be useful to both protagonists: to the subject because they will remove his prejudices and put him in a favorable frame of mind, and to the hypnotist because they will inform him about his subject's mental attitude and about any obstacles that could possibly arise. For example, if the very word "hypnosis" frightens the subject, the hypnotist can then propose to demonstrate the power of suggestion to him. If the word "suggestion" also terrifies him, then the hypnotist can limit himself to promising to demonstrate by a simple experiment the way in which the idea of movement can become transformed into movement. Here are some examples:

The backward postural sway: The hypnotist asks the subject to stand very relaxed with his back to him and to look straight ahead. He then asks the subject to close his eyes and listen carefully to what he is going to say. Then, placing his hands flat on the subject's shoulder blades (or just one hand between the shoulder blades) without exerting any pressure, the hypnotist warns him that when he removes his hands, an irresistible force will draw his body backward. The subject is told not to fear this movement because the hypnotist will prevent him from falling. After this preliminary demonstration comes the experiment itself, during which the hypnotist fires a continuous barrage of suggestions at the subject because his presence must be constantly felt if he is to monopolize the subject's intellect. Almost the same words are repeated for as long as the procedure lasts and until it is successful: "You are concentrating on what I am telling you. You do not hear anything but my voice, you are falling backward . . . you cannot help yourself . . . a force is pulling you backward

James Braid proves that hypnotic sleep requires neither the presence of a magnetizer nor the existence of a fluid—*Holzapfel*

. . ." A few moments later, or occasionally a few minutes later, one out of two subjects will topple backward, but the hypnotist is there to prevent a fall.

The forward postural sway: The same procedure can be used for the forward postural sway. The hypnotist tells the subject to look him straight in the eyes, and directs his gaze at the bridge of the subject's nose. He places his hands on the subject's shoulders and gives more or less the same instructions as for the backward postural sway. However, the backward postural sway is the preferred procedure, as it is easier to obtain.

The Chevreul pendulum was invented by Chevreul, a famous chemist. This experiment consists of holding a bright object dangling from a thread over a ruler. The hypnotist tells the subject that the pendulum is going to swing in the same direction as the ruler is lying, no matter how great his effort to keep it motionless. This test usually works quite quickly.

Clasped hands. This test, which is both fast and effective, has the advantage of being able to be used on several subjects at the same time, and it permits the operator to move straight into the induction procedure. It is also very popular with stage hypnotists because it allows them to judge immediately the suitability of the volunteers who have come onto the stage to participate in the experiment. (We should add that these volunteers are always set up by the announcers, who have made certain of their hypnotizability or their ability to simulate as a last resort.) The operator asks the subjects to clasp their hands together on their knees, on top of their heads, or above their heads, with the fingers tightly interlocked. He tells them to listen carefully to his words and to concentrate on what he is telling them. He then suggests that the subjects' hands are so tightly clasped together that they cannot be separated. This suggestion works in all good subjects who really concentrate.

METHODS OF INDUCING HYPNOSIS

Preparation. Once the subject has been convinced by use of the postural-sway or pendulum test that the idea of movement can easily be transformed into movement, or, better still, once the subject's hands have remained clasped tightly together, the hypnotist must now persuade him that hypnosis can be very beneficial. He must assure the subject that he is running no risks; that, at worst, it will do him neither harm nor good; and that therefore he can have complete confidence in the hypnotist. The subject must be convinced that his full cooperation is necessary and that, above all, he must not try to study what is happening or analyze what he is experiencing. This persuasion should be personal and measured, adapted to each individual so as not to anger or shock him. A lot of finesse, insight, and adroitness is needed to be a good hypnotist. This is true for all practices where an appeal is made to the subject's intelligence. Coarse, self-willed operators only succeed in irritating their subjects and encouraging them to be contrary.

Fascination. In the case of weak or timid people who collapse helplessly, fascination is an exception where the preparation procedure is useless. Sir Henry Stanley, the explorer, related that when he was being threatened by a large group of natives, he ordered a blank to be fired from a small cannon that he was carrying in his baggage. At the sound of the detonation, all the natives fell to the ground, stricken with terror and as incapable of reacting as the beetles that feign death when turned over on their backs.

But this happened in Africa, over a century ago. Today the chances of paralyzing a whole group with fear by making a thunderous noise are pretty slim. Violent measures are even less recommended. Yet fascination still retains its power. Certainly a hypnotist can no longer say "Sleep!" in the menacing way used by Faria, who would force his subjects to avert their eyes under the pressure of his own gazing. But there are still operators who begin by gazing steadily at the subject without blinking until the subject closes his eyes, while at the same time continually repeating suggestions. This is obviously a method requiring a lot of experience and authority, but it allows those who use it to hypnotize under almost any conditions.

The surroundings. The hypnotist should try to assemble favorable conditions, such as: a warm temperature (about 74° F.) with no drafts; physical comfort, the subject either lying on a couch or settled in an armchair (standing is a last resort); one bright spot in a room with subdued lighting; and a repetitive, monotonous sound (the ticking of a clock or a metronome or the humming of a machine can provide a suitable background). It is not advisable to use a complex appliance, as this can distract the subject's attention because of its mechanical nature or by misfiring.

As far as surroundings are concerned, Luys's revolving mirror and Bérillon's tremulant armchair were combined with all sorts of sonorous accessories—tomtoms, Chinese gongs, whistles, tuning forks—which, though lacking in harmony, gave variety to the Salpêtrière experiments.

Charcot and his associates worked with cases of *grande hystérie* in whom any intense excitation immediately caused catalepsy. For these inmates, any unusual noise was a signal for them to go into a trance. Was this obligingness or simulation? Not necessarily. The ease with which some hysterical females can be hypnotized should warn us not to judge rashly this period of hypnotism when somnambulism was in such great esteem that the idea of falling into a swoon under the control of a magnetizer obsessed many women's minds.

When Brouardel (1837–1906) testified as an authority on hypnosis in the case of a dentist from Rouen, France, who had seduced a young girl while her mother was at the other end of the same room, he made it known during his testimony that the dentist had placed the young victim at his mercy in less than forty-five seconds by putting her into a state of hypnosis. He had asked her to look up with her head back. Then he put her to sleep by exerting pressure on her eyeballs.

This method, which was discovered by Lasègue (1816–1883), a pathologist, usually succeeds only with hysterical patients, but there are exceptions. Most subjects require hypnosis to be induced progressively, without contact and in fact, solely by the use of suggestion. The old methods are still of interest, and occasionally so are their masters because the results obtained by the great pioneers have proven their effectiveness. There are still some practitioners who believe in the influence of passes (hand movements made in front of the subject's eyes and close to his body). They continue to be effective even if only on the imagination, that precious ally of suggestion.

On the other hand, the exploitation of hysterogenic zones has been given up. The transfer of the hysterogenic zones by the

Charcot's first experiments with magnetism at Salpêtrière—*Corson*

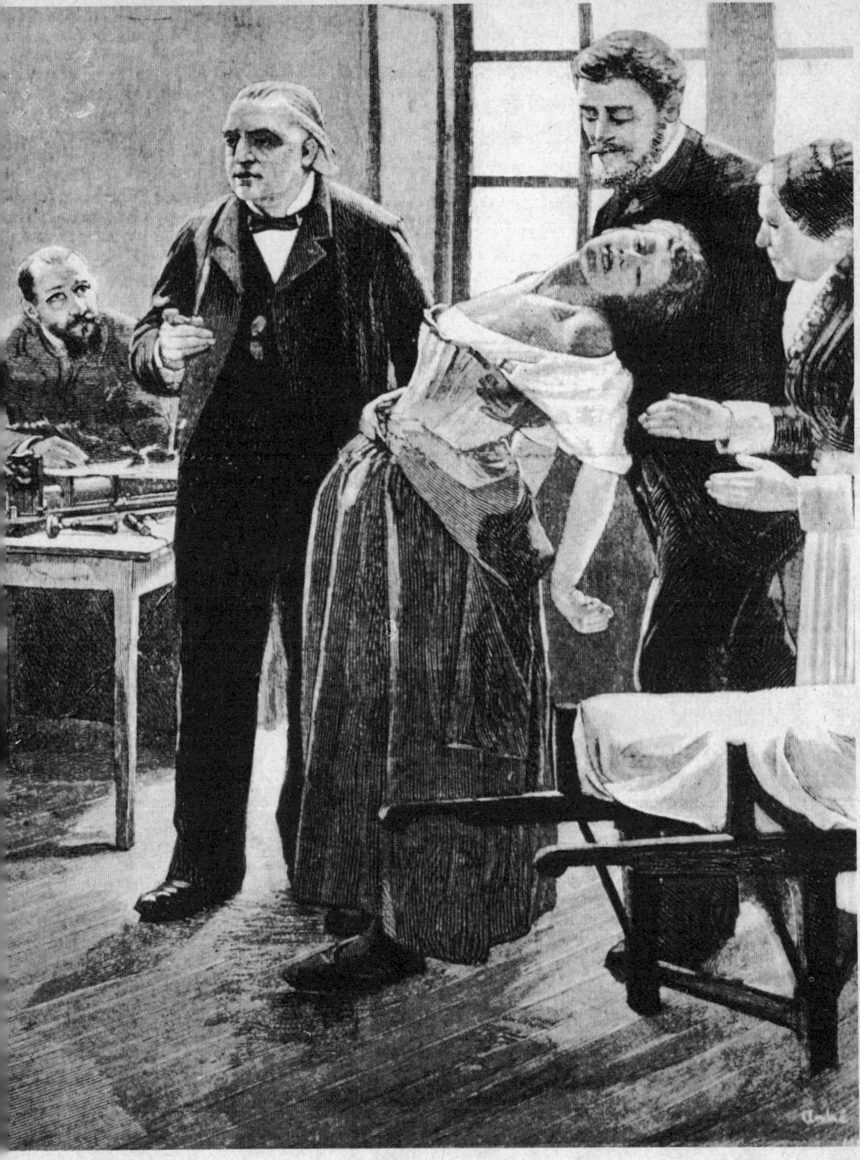

use of magnets often used to transform Salpêtrière into an erotic laboratory. According to the Salpêtrière studies, the hysterogenic zones "have definite analogies with the erogenous zones, for simply touching them when the patient is in a provoked somnambulistic state creates genital sensations strong enough to cause an orgasm. Only sensitive during total somnambulism, the erogenous zone is transferable by magnets" (Binet and Féré). There is a list of these zones in Appendix 3.

HYPNOTIZATION: THE BEGINNING

Every hypnotist has his own method, but all the methods concur and it is only in the way they commence that there are variations. Here are the three principal methods, which are often used in association with one another.

Exploitation of the demonstration test. This procedure is the most useful when the hypnotist can take advantage of contagion, which is a prime asset. It begins with the "clasped hands" demonstration. This can be performed on a whole group and then the subjects can be treated in their order of suggestibility.

If the hypnotist has only one subject lying back in an armchair or reclining on a couch, it is more advisable to make the subject clasp his hands and hold them on his chest, with the fingers laced together. It is less tiring to hold this position, which is maintained by very light traction of the biceps, than it is to lift the arms upward, a movement that stems from the shoulders. This is why the suggestion that the subject can no longer unclasp his hands has a better chance of working; the hands-on-chest position concurs with the law of least effort.

The hypnotist then proposes a series of inhibitions, for example: "You will now be able to unclasp your hands, but you cannot utter a sound." In order to heighten the demonstration, it is possible even to transpose this commanded powerlessness to certain parts of the memory, thus: "You have forgotten your address!" But every conscientious hypnotist must remember to correct everything he has even slightly distorted by suggestion. He must be careful not to propose too many inhibitions. Although he may rely on contagion to induce hypnosis in the whole group, he will nevertheless stress the heaviness of the atmosphere, the feeling of listlessness that they are all feeling, and the heaviness of the eyelids, which desire to close. The effect will also depend on the fact that the hypnotist announces what the subjects are witnessing.

Fixed gazing. This was Braid's method. With this method, the hypnotist has a sure knowledge of the phenomena that are going to occur when the subject gazes fixedly at a bright object or a mark on the ceiling. Preferably the subject is lying down. "Your eyelids are beginning to feel heavy. Your eyes are blinking, they are getting moist. You cannot see distinctly, your eyes are closed . . ." These were Bernheim's phrases and then he finally added: "You are sleeping!"—a phrase that is generally avoided today, for we prefer to suggest to the subject that he is relaxing, that he feels completely at ease, and that he feels so much better like this, detached from everything, etc. The subject's surrender is preceded by a quivering of the eyes, which is so characteristic that some authors (Esdaile, Liébeault, Burgess) called it cataleptic. After this, the subject, who is reassured by the fact that everything is happening exactly as the hypnotist said it would, will now accept his commands.

Gradual relaxation. In this purely verbal procedure, the subject, who is lying comfortably in a position conducive to sleep, accepts the suggestions to relax all his muscles as much as he can, starting with the feet and legs, then the body, and finally the muscles of the face and eyes.

The current practice is to combine the above methods. Many hypnotists believe that it is necessary to explain in detail all the symptoms that the subject will feel in the course of his drowsiness, untiringly and with no fear of boring the subject through repetition, since monotony is a factor in inducing hypnosis. If the subject does not feel them, it is sufficient if he believes what he is being told, as the effect is identical. So the subject needs a lot of conviction in order to assure himself that he believes it.

But the hypnotist must not rely too heavily on his powers of elocution. He must be very careful to avoid using any words that could surprise or irritate and therefore alert the subject's mind. Just as there are words that create optimism, so there are words that disseminate anxiety and confusion, for example, "pain," "worry," "distressing." These must be avoided just like the words evoking sleep, in which the patient is liable not to believe.

Some practitioners pride themselves on not being long-winded and on using reserve, but only experience enables one to achieve mastery.

Like the preceding methods, these following techniques all link up at more or less the same point—the slight trance—and this is where the rapport between the subject and the hypnotist is established.

A slow method: hypnosis by levitation of the hand (Erickson's method). The patient sits comfortably in a chair with the palms of his hands on his thighs or on a table. He is told to observe his hands very closely, to keep watching them and to concentrate on all the sensations and feelings in the hands, no matter what they may be. Soon, a slight motion or jerking develops in one of the fingers or in the hand. Then the subject is told that the spaces between the fingers will widen and that the fingers will slowly move apart. This is the first real suggestion to which the patient is expected to respond. If the fingers start spreading apart, the patient is now in a state of suggestibility. He will react to the suggestion that his arm is going to rise by raising his hand, then his forearm, and finally the arm itself. Thus he is convinced by this obvious proof that the suggestion is working. Making him close his eyes is then a mere formality.

A rapid method: instantaneous induction (Whitlow's method). Derived from a procedure employed by stage hypnotists, this method consists of provoking temporary cerebral ischemia in the subject by exerting pressure with the right thumb and index finger on both sides of the Adam's apple, on the vagus nerve and the carotid arteries. Meanwhile, with the left hand, pressure is applied behind both ears just below the mastoid process. This causes dizziness. At the same time, the hypnotist fires a stream of suggestions at the subject, who, having been suddenly brought to the verge of unconsciousness, is very open to suggestion. But this method is dangerous.

Induction during sleep. This method, which consists of murmuring to a subject sleeping a natural sleep, that, without waking, he is going to listen to the hypnotist's instructions, is a last resort for stubborn subjects. Wagner included a scene of this type in *The Twilight of the Gods,* Act II, scene 1.

THE RAPPORT BETWEEN HYPNOTIST AND SUBJECT

Traditionally, the term "rapport" has been used to mean the condition of affinity between the subject and the hypnotist that is present at the onset of hypnosis and that precludes the subject's relating to anything other than the hypnotist himself unless he instructs the subject otherwise. Such close rapport was said to have been obtained that words and gestures became superfluous. The hypnotist could even transmit thoughts to his subject. This no doubt can be explained by the increased attention the subject would give to the hypnotist's slightest gestures. Esdaile, who performed surgery under hypnosis on any patient who came to him needing surgery, denied the necessity of this relationship. After giving up metallotherapy, Charcot believed mainly in material media for inducing hypnosis, and since he himself did not hypnotize, he did not insist on its usefulness. Today, however, hypnotherapy emphasizes a collaboration between the practitioner and the subject, the former actively and the latter passively. And since their common purpose is to effect a beneficial and curative treatment, the rapport becomes both useful and desirable. But it is not necessary to see it as a manifestation of transference, as some hypnotists of the psychoanalytical school do.

THE SLIGHT TRANCE

Our description has reached the point where the subject has his eyes closed. This is only the beginning. The subject is now in a hypnoidal state and is approaching what is called the slight trance.

The slight trance will be more pronounced if the subject cannot open his eyes unless the operator orders him to do so. It is wise to tell the subject this, but in such a way that he will not try to defy the operator. So long as he believes what he is told, that is enough.

The subject is also beginning to feel a certain lethargy in his limbs. If the operator tells him, "You can no longer raise your arm," he will readily admit it. It is possible that on waking he will claim that he did not move his arm because of sheer laziness, but the fact remains that he did not raise his arm. He obeyed. In the light trance the subject is in a sleeplike attitude that he will be able to maintain, staying motionless no matter what his position, for much longer than an ordinary sleeping person can.

It is now possible and even useful as a control test to make the subject's position even more unusual. For example, if the operator raises the subject's arm, the limb will remain in that position. This rigidity is classified among the phenomena called "catalepsy," a term that has never been defined with the accuracy that we would desire. However, at this stage, some subjects become so completely relaxed that their limbs are like soft wax. Hence the name *flexibilitas cerea* has been given to this condition.

These cataleptic phenomena illustrate the progress of the trance, so it is therefore unnecessary to encourage the subject to raise his arm or to open his eyes, as this is never without risks. If the subject should regain possession of himself just to be contrary, then the hypnotist would start to lose his self-confidence and would probably have to postpone the attempt until another time.

Some hypnotists working under more ideal conditions—for example, in hospital clinics—believe these control checks are unnecessary, especially since they involve phenomena varying from subject to subject and from operator to operator.

If the hypnotist insists on attempting this check and even if he is almost sure of its success, it is better to introduce it in a nonaffirmative way. For example, it is preferable to say, "Your hand is heavy . . . it is very heavy . . . you have no desire to raise it," rather than to say, "You cannot raise your hand." The subject's passivity confirms this state of suggestibility and if, by chance, he does decide to raise his hand and succeeds, it is not important. The operator had not told him it was impossible.

Another method of verification that is unlikely to jeopardize the experiment and that has the advantage of increasing the subject's submissiveness is, according to Liébeault's terminology, "rotatory automatism" (automatic rotary movements). This consists of taking the subject's wrists and making him turn his hands around each other (as we twiddle our thumbs). If hypnosis has been induced, once the movement has been started, it can be stopped only by the hypnotist's orders, Liébeault considered this loss of control as a definite sign of a "deeper light sleep" and a signal that the "intermediary light sleep," or medium trance, was approaching.

The slight trance, frequently achieved at the first attempt, involves no loss of consciousness. If the subject is questioned after the sitting, he will not fail to show some doubts or to claim that he did not really lose consciousness, that he heard everything, and that, consequently, the demonstration leaves him skeptical.

Nevertheless, it is definite that a subject can be influenced in a slight trance and that, from a practical point of view, suggestions can be effectively accepted. Both Braid and Liébeault knew this. And, based on the experiences of one century, we can affirm the therapeutic usefulness of the slight trance.

THE MEDIUM TRANCE

If possible, it is good to progress further than a light trance. First, the operator can suggest partial amnesia to the patient (occasionally it occurs without his having to suggest it). He can also take advantage of a curious phenomenon that vaudeville hypnotists readily exploit: "glove" anesthesia, in which the hand is insensitive to burning and pricking, just as though it were gloved. Spectators who see the operator sticking a needle into the subject's hand are amazed. As for the subject, even though he has no memory of the experiment because of the partial amnesia, there is a small hole in the skin where the needle was inserted (generally between the thumb and the index finger) and thus he must acknowledge both the prick and his loss of consciousness.

It is always in this state of medium trance (the province of vaudeville hypnotists) that cataleptic rigidity permits astonishing feats. With his body rigid, a subject who is stretched out between two chairs can, without feeling it, support a weight that would double him up like a jackknife in his normal waking state. Some spectators have even seen a stone block broken on the thoracic cage of a frail woman who was balanced between two supports. (In one case they saw the stone breaker miss his shot and smash the face of the poor woman, the wife of the hypnotist. The job of being a trained subject is not with risks.)

It is also during the medium trance that sensory illusions begin—illusions of taste, smell, and touch—which can be used very humorously on the stage.

"Your chair is on fire!" the hypnotist cries. The subject leaps up.

"Taste this orange." The subject feasts on a raw potato.

"Smell this rose." And the subject takes pleasure in smelling a piece of putrid cheese.

These pranks that amuse the public should not make us forget that in this stage of hypnosis doctors have obtained some excellent results. In addition to very increased suggestibility, partial amnesia can be exploited for certain psychotherapeutic treatments.

Since the slight trance is generally sufficient for salutary suggestions to be accepted, it is therefore not often necessary to push hypnosis further. The operator should seek a more complete hold over the subject's mind only when this can be more effective. Somnambulism is manifested in the deep trance along with phenomena that used to constitute "deep hypnotism" at Salpêtrière.

THE DEEP TRANCE

Generally speaking, the subject who has accepted suggestions deceiving the senses remembers nothing when he awakes. According to many authors, this total amnesia is situated either at the culminating point of the medium trance or at the threshold of the deep, or somnambulistic, trance. The first characteristic of the deep trance is not so much loss of memory as the subject's ability to open his eyes without affecting the depth of the trance. It is wise to warn him that he is going to see but that he is not going to wake up. He should also be told that he must pay attention only to what the hypnotist is saying and see only what the hypnotist tells him to see.

From now on, he will not only see what the hypnotist wishes him to see but also what the hypnotist suggests he can see; or he will see persons and objects in the light that the hypnotist describes them. The subject can even be made to believe he can see things where there is nothing. It goes without saying that it is easier to make him believe that the nurse is his favorite movie star than to suggest out of the clear blue sky that his favorite movie star is in the room. In fact, this last suggestion involves an additional effort on the part of the subject's intellect, which at this particular stage is not performing its characteristic activity, but is at the stage where personality dissociations and regressions in age occur. We shall refer to these two phenomena again. Visual and auditory hallucinations (the latter being more difficult to obtain) are therefore a criterion of the somnambulistic trance.

The deep trance can show two aspects in its development. One is passive, in which the subject sinks into a sort of lethargy from which he is loath to emerge. With his eyes closed, he replies in a thick voice with indistinct words. The other aspect is active. If the hypnotist tells the subject to open his eyes, he hesitates at first as though his sight were foggy, then, opening his eyes, he sees in a vague, dim way. At this stage of hypnosis the body is not rigid. It can even be slightly limp, and the subject's bearing is like that of a sleepwalker. The subject can speak and often does without being asked. He converses freely and even fluently, as did the Marquis de Puységur's patient, Victor, who was the very first artificial somnambulist. Although the active and passive states are very different, they are close enough that a passive subject can become active if the hypnotist advises him not to sleep and to open his eyes. However, this instruction, which goes against his natural tendencies, runs the risk of waking him completely.

POSTHYPNOTIC SUGGESTION

It is certainly strange to see an individual transformed into a somnambulist or to see him perceive things that do not exist.

The most interesting aspect, however, is that in this state hypnotic suggestions are accepted no matter how great the delay before they are to be carried out. Forgetting everything that has happened during the sitting is easy for the hypnotist to impose, but he must be most careful to make sure that all his directions are carried out on time. Strangely enough, when he has terminated the hypnosis and consequently suspended the rapport, the practitioner generally cannot erase a posthypnotic suggestion without putting the subject back into a trance.

One hypnotist suggested to a subject that ten minutes after awaking he would open the window to breathe. After the sitting, the hypnotist started speaking about the nice, fresh room so as to be able to bring in the words: "You don't need to open the window. We have plenty of air. In fact, it is rather chilly." The subject agreed. The conversation changed, then suddenly the subject stood up. "I wonder if it is really as cloudy as that outside," he said, opening the window. And after taking a good deep breath, he added, "The fresh air is good, isn't it?"

The first posthypnotic suggestion, usually given to the subject when he is in a medium trance, will cause him to go back into a hypnotic state spontaneously at the first prearranged signal from the hypnotist (and from him alone). A number or a sound will serve adequately as the signal.

Posthypnotic suggestion is no doubt the most disconcerting phenomenon of hypnosis. It is not without humor, because suggestions that lay the subject open to ridicule are carried out as conscientiously as reasonable orders. The story of a man who, in spite of sunshine and a blue sky, insisted on opening his umbrella at midday in the main square of the town has often been repeated.

The medical importance of posthypnotic suggestion is obvious. It allows us to envisage many treatments, insofar as the nervous system can be used as a therapeutic agent—and it often can.

This interesting experiment was performed in a mental hospital. A doctor hypnotized and suggested to his night attendants to awake the instant a lunatic attempted to get out of bed. Sounds that had no reference to the attendants' duties were inhibited by suggestion, while any sounds relating to the inmates' movements were rendered more acute by posthypnotic suggestion, with the result that the attendants slept well and performed their duties with perfect vigilance and without being unduly fatigued.

This delayed response to suggestions is one of the most valuable aspects of hypnotic therapy. We do not know where it starts, since from the very early stages of hypnosis the subject can be influenced in a salutary way (but obviously not spontaneously). Nor do we know where it ends or where it goes to, because no one has thoroughly exploited it.

At the end of the last century there were some subjects living most of their lives under hypnosis. They lived a normal life, awake of course, but continually in conformity with their hypnotist's instructions. As soon as they were no longer under the influence of suggestion, they would fall back into the state of degeneration and neglect from which hypnosis had successfully removed them. Such clearcut cases are rare, and it is impossible to set forth here the infinite variety of mental states and suffering, anguish, and diseases of all kinds that can be improved. It is sufficient to note that an enormous amount of the knowledge now known in psychoanalysis and psychosomatic medicine had its origin in hypnosis. After splitting from hypnosis, these therapies are now returning to it in a definite but often circuitous way. There has been a particular resurgence in the use of posthypnotic suggestion in these specialties.

There are countless ways of terminating hypnosis. Usually the operator will say, "I am going to count to five and you will wake up." However, before doing this, he must correct everything he has modified. Not only must he flex the patient's arm if he had convinced the subject of its rigidity, but he must also insist that all the subject's organs are functioning well. He must clear the subject's mind of all the hallucinations that could possibly have been suggested to him. For we never know what disturbing consequences might result from suggestions that have not been erased from the subject's mind.

Some practitioners snap their fingers. Others blow on the patient's forehead or eyes. According to Braid, a current of fresh air would channel the subject's attention to the epidermis, so he was no longer held in a hypnotic state by his concentration on one idea. At Salpêtrière, by using a fan to mask half the face of trained hysterical female patients, the operators were even able to only half awake them. Does this mean that the subject can show a half-sleep of this kind if the hypnotist wakes him by blowing on him from one side? Obviously not. The subject will either awake fully or not at all. In the latter case, which is very rare, the hypnotist should let him sleep. The subject will pass from a hypnotic sleep to a normal sleep and will awake naturally sooner or later.

FATAL HYPNOSIS

Accidents are very rare, but we should point out that they have occurred, if only to warn amateurs of the risks involved for the people on whom they are practicing. Volgyesi states that in Budapest in 1895, a woman was put into the deepest stages of an absolute trance by a lay hypnotist and that she remained in such a deep hypnotic coma that she could not be awakened. She died in the same way that Preyer's frog almost died on the rope.

Not much is known about the fatal trance because luckily we have not had much experience with it. In 1889 a Spanish practitioner, Sanchez Herrero, claimed that he could kill a subject by suggesting to him under hypnosis that his heart was going to stop beating. No one volunteered for this suicidal experiment.

Seabrook recounts the existence of strange creatures in Haiti called zombies. They are supposedly dead people whom men gifted with a certain power disinter before their bodies putrefy. They are reanimated and kept in slavery to provide free labor. According to Seabrook, they must not eat meat or any food containing salt, otherwise they suddenly become aware of their condition and relentlessly seek to go back to their tombs.

It is easy to poke fun at the people believing in zombies and to label stories of this kind as old wives' tales. Seabrook, who was very skeptical, actually saw these "living dead" working on a sugar plantation, but the woman guarding them refused to let him speak to them. He first thought that they were lunatics or idiots. But then, in Port-au-Prince, he learned from Dr. Antoine Villiers that nobody in Haiti treated this matter lightly, not even the criminal code of the country. According to Article 249: "Any administration to persons of substances which, without causing death, provoke a more or less prolonged sleep will be considered as attempted murder. And the fact of burying a person alive to whom such substances have been administered will be considered as murder *regardless of whether the person lives or dies.*"

HYPNOSIS THROUGH DRUGS

In addition to the rather startling provisions of the Haitian criminal code, what catches our attention are the words "substances that provoke . . . prolonged sleep." This exempts hypnosis, because sleep caused by a chemical agent is generally called narcosis.

Many practitioners are against the use of drugs to induce hypnosis. They say that if the subject cannot be hypnotized normally, it is because nature is protecting him either directly or indirectly through the intermediary of the subconscious: therefore, it is better not to insist on hypnotizing him.

Among the products that are said to help provoke hypnosis, the best known is scopochlarose, a mixture of scopolamine, hydrobromide, and chloralose, developed by Brotteaux in 1928. At the beginning of this century, Bramwell mentioned the use of hashish (accidentally used by Esdaile), chloroform (which is very effective on stubborn patients), chloral, and morphine. Mescaline, which is made from peyote and causes colored dreams and hallucinations, was not well known at that time. With specialties in medicine being the present vogue, we could draw up a much more extensive list of sedatives, hypnotics, and narcotics (the famous "truth serum" is classified as one of these).

All these drugs probably produce one moment when the subject's defenses are relaxed, he is impressionable or suggestible as he is falling asleep. This phase is usually quite brief, so it is difficult to detect and exploit it. We still are not sure whether these drugs cause changes in the personality or, in particular, if they alter areas of the personality that we would like to influence. So we can readily understand the cautiousness of some hypnotists, and even their hostility, toward drugs.

CHAPTER VIII

Hypnosis and Its Use in Medicine

IN 1780, magnetism could cure everything.

In 1830, somnanbulism could cure everything.

In 1890, hypnotism could cure almost everything.

In 1960, hypnosis cured nothing at all.

Hypnotists today have learned modesty through the disappointments of their predecessors. Many of them admit that their art is like a coat of paint over the rust: it covers the damage, but the damage is still there. This is especially true if we equate hypnosis only with suggestion, or if we choose to see in hypnosis nothing more than a technique having a psychological influence. Then, hypnosis would have only the same value as other therapies appealing to the imagination and producing results.

Hypnotists themselves admit that efficacious treatments are rare when not incorporated with psychoanalysis and psychosomatic medicine. It is in association with these therapies that hypnosis has made its way into the medical world. Anyone can hypnotize, but those who can cure, or claim they can cure, by using hypnosis alone are asking for trouble. Consequently, apart from its action on pain (which anesthesia has made almost unnecessary), medicine today acknowledges that hypnosis puts the subject into a state where the operator must be either a psychoanalyst or a specialist in psychosomatic disorders to obtain convincing results.

Thus, even if it is considered only in terms of the therapies that are combined with it, hypnosis can retrieve its heritage. After all, when it became hypnotism, it managed to recover the ground that it had formerly lost as magnetism, then as somnambulism. Let us hope for a similar revival with its use in psychosomatic medicine.

INTERACTION OF THE MIND AND THE BODY

This new branch of medicine originated around 1935 in the United States, where hypnotism had for a long time been discredited because of the questionable performances of stage hypnotists. The founder of psychosomatic medicine, Dr. H. Flanders Dunbar, was trying to find subjects who were not depressed in order to compare them with her own patients. Her first thought was to look for them among accident victims, in people whose malady had not yet had time to undermine their spirits. But she was surprised to note that, generally speaking, if these subjects were in good physical health, the same could not be said about their mental state. Their accidents seemed to have been inscribed in their psyches in advance. Dr. Dunbar found these victims of fate to be rebels, individuals who had become defiant as the result of too strict an upbringing and who were always in conflict with society. Unconsciously, they had wished for their accidents, and the accident brought them relief. She concluded from this that if a state of mind can cause someone to be accident-prone, then it is likely that a similar state of mind could determine organic disorders.

The relationship between the body and the mind has been known throughout all the ages, with greater or less emphasis depending on the trends of the period, and hypnotists too have studied it.

A relatively unknown author, Dr. Géraud Bonnet, who had a degree in mathematics and physical science and who was a persistent investigator, published a dissertation on hypnotism in 1923. This was a time when boldness like his could only discredit him. He wrote:

> Sorrow, great joy, and emotions can cause palpitations, urinary complaints, dyspeptic, bilious and intestinal disorders. These ailments, which are transitory at first, can become permanent,

causing more serious organic lesions if the causative agent is recurrent.

And thus a morbid condition of psychic origin can be established and it is wrong to attribute this to bacterial infection.

Therefore, in all diagnoses, it is both necessary and advantageous to distinguish clearly between the psychic aberration on the one hand and the organic lesion on the other; and, if possible, to determine if the disease began by a psychic alteration or by an organic disorder.

Suggestion always has a direct influence on the organic lesion. It has an indirect influence on the additional symptoms accompanying the disease and on the psychic or organic lesions. By acting on, and helping to regulate physical functioning, suggestion can cause a change in the psychic lesion and thus contribute to the subject's recovery.

The following lines could have been written in the first circular sent out by Dr. Flanders when she was inviting her colleagues to look for psychic origins in the diseases they were treating. Mesmer's admirers, who had gathered to celebrate his birthday on May 23, 1850, were already proclaiming these origins in unison:

It's the nerves, nerves, nerves,
Which turn the universe,
It's through the nerves, nerves, nerves,
That we possess the universe.

And, Galen claimed in the second century, more prosaically, that the temples of Aesculapius provided the proof that many serious diseases could be cured solely by mental shock. So, hypnosis can link up with psychosomatic medicine with no fears. Historically, it was Freud who ensured this transition.

A FRENCH ANALYSIS

The Nancy school regarded the contributions of hypnosis to medicine as considerable. In his work *La Suggestion* (1891), Bernheim classified the diseases able to be influenced by suggestion under the following headings: organic disorders of the nervous system (hemiplegia, multiple sclerosis, cerebrospinal sclerosis, lead poisoning); hysterical disorders, neuropathic disorders, and neuroses (chorea, somnambulism, incontinence); pareses and paralyses, gastrointestinal disorders, various pains, rheumatic diseases, neuralgia, and menstrual disorders.

And Liébeault, making a similar analysis of hypnotism's contribution to medicine, added cures of anemia, intermittent fever, and tuberculosis. These are diseases that are obviously caused by bacteria, but Liébeault did not take this into consideration. This great pioneer of hypnotism may have listed a strange collection of hypnotic cures, but these same cures, observed and verified, can be found in all the literature of that period.

AN ENGLISH ANALYSIS (1900)

Bramwell, an Englishman who at the end of last century made a detailed analysis of the results obtained by hypnosis in both medicine and surgery, mentioned extraordinary cures of anemia of hysterical origin. For example, a patient who was extremely emaciated and unable to walk was declared incurable after receiving counterirritation from many heat applications. But after the third hypnotic sitting, he could walk, and by the end of the week he had exchanged his wheelchair for a bicycle.

We cannot recount all the cures mentioned by Bramwell. His list does not coincide exactly with Bernheim's because he did not include organic disorders of the nervous system. But all the other complaints, and more, are listed: all types of hysteria, tremors, spasms, involuntary quivering of the eyelids, paralyses, chronic torticollis, amaurosis, mutism, constipation or dyspepsia, St. Vitus' dance (chorea), stammering, moistness of the hands, neurasthenia, obsessions—all yielded to hypnosis more often than they resisted it.

Bramwell is not so categorical about hypnotic cures for insanity, alcoholism, and morphine addiction. In this last domain, his own results were very unsatisfactory. But his colleague, Wetterstrand, had by 1896 obtained thirty-seven lasting cures out of a total of fifty-one hypnotized patients. The patients were treated at home. The sittings were held twice daily and deep hypnosis was induced whenever possible. The morphia was decreased gradually, and injections of water instead of morphine were

Ambroise-Auguste Liébeault (1823-1904)—*Holzapfel*

scrupulously avoided. Later, Wetterstrand obtained even better results from drug addicts who were in nursing homes; he obtained cures through prolonged sleep by suggestion.

And so, on both sides of the English Channel at the end of the nineteenth century, men agreed on the vast possibilities open to hypnosis, And yet, between Liébeault's and Bramwell's reports, there had been Pasteur's great discoveries of bacteria, which, he proved, are found everywhere. So it was impossible that some of the cures were obtained by suggestion alone.

A GERMAN ANALYSIS (1928)

In his revision of Hirschfass' *Treatise on Hypnotism and Suggestive Therapy* in 1928, T. H. Schultz, the inventor of autogenic training, noted that the condition of patients suffering from consumption was improved by hypnotically suppressing the painful symptoms localized in various parts of the body. He also mentioned the treatment of chronic or severe rheumatism, influenza, and asthma of nervous origin, on the obvious condition that if the deep cause of the malady was not known, the therapy could treat only the symptoms. Schultz added to his list of conditions treatable by suggestion:

Pain
All types of spasms
Paralyses and contractures
Hysterical disturbances of sensitivity
Nervous disorders of the digestive system
Intestinal irregularities
Insomnia of nervous origin
Mental imbalances
Phobias
Obsessions
Tics
Psychosexual anomalies
Morbid tendencies
Functional language disorders
Organic diseases

Schultz's list in no way invalidates Bernheim's classification of 1890. We no longer draw up lists like this today, not because hypnosis no longer cures, but because the contribution of psychoanalysis has slightly altered the treatments. They are conducted much more ingeniously, for we now possess information about the deep origins and "motivations" of diseases that was unknown in Bernheim's time. Doctors utilizing hypnosis therefore prefer to minimize its role and attribute their success to psychoanalysis or, even more readily, to psychosomatic medicine (which has created fewer enemies).

THE ENIGMAS OF THE AUTONOMIC NERVOUS SYSTEM

Hypnosis exercises a definite influence on the autonomic nervous system. For a long time, little was known about this nervous system that controls our vegetative life. We know that it is through the cerebrospinal nervous system that we perceive sensations and that our movements are controlled. But there is no voluntary control over breathing and digestion; these functions of the autonomic nervous system continue to operate whether we are asleep or awake. The machinery of the hundreds of muscles that we control through the intervention of our voluntary nervous system is insignificant compared to the countless highly complex mechanisms that are controlled by the autonomic nervous system: miles of blood vessels, whose diameter must be adjusted according to the needs of the moment; all the movements involved in digestion, from the esophagus to the intestine; the body temperature, which remains fixed regardless of the environmental temperature or the activity in which the body is involved; the functions of the heart and lungs; the secretion of saliva; and many other functions about which very little is known.

It often happens that it is the invention of a mechanism similar to a natural phenomenon that makes us understand it; for example, radar, which demonstrated that bats guide themselves by echoes; the amazing speed of line-by-line exploration with electronic points and television screens (where there are several hundreds of thousands of points per image and tens of millions of points per second, which destroyed the idea that our eyes encompass the whole visual field with one glance. It is possible, then, that our autonomic nervous system, which must respond simultaneously to all sorts of stimulations, works in a way that is far beyond our intellectual understanding. It would therefore be impossible for us to regulate its functioning ourselves. Moreover, it would almost certainly break down under our control because we are far from being able to define the role of its most subtle piece of machinery: the endocrine glands, which influence the functioning of certain organs by the secretion of chemical substances called hormones.

THE ACTION OF HYPNOSIS ON THE AUTONOMIC NERVOUS SYSTEM

That this high-precision mechanism has a more or less autonomous life and that it is not under our voluntary control does not mean, however, that it is not possible for us to influence it. For example, Hindu fakirs can reverse the digestive process. On the stage, fakirs and hypnotists have often shown that they can stop a wound from bleeding. This voluntary control over hemorrhaging is currently utilized by "hypnodentists."

In laboratory experiments we have been able to slow down or accelerate cardiac rhythm through the use of hypnotic suggestion. Likewise, by suggesting to the subject that he is eating, we can provoke the secretion of gastric juices, the acidity of which will vary according to the type of food suggested to the subject. Movements of the esophagus and intestines have also been started under hypnosis; the superior orifice of the stomach has been opened; the amount of calcium in the blood has been modified; and by suggesting to diabetic subjects that their pancreas is functioning better, we have been able to reduce the percentage of sugar in their blood by half. It is easy to produce goose pimples in a subject by suggesting that he is cold. Through suggestions given at daily sittings, we have also been able to increase the basal metabolism of an obese patient suffering from myxedema, with the result that his weight returned to normal. And finally, intestinal secretion of enzymes has been modified through hypnosis.

These various results all concern phenomena that are dependent on the autonomic nervous system and glands, such as the pancreas and the thyroid. We ourselves have no control over them and, in fact, do not really know what controls them. We should not overestimate the effect of hypnosis. But even if experiments are not cures, they do open up a whole range of possibilities that are still unexplored.

THE SO-CALLED SMALL PROBLEMS OF MEDICINE

The best medical practitioners concede that suggestion can on occasion make warts disappear and prevent children from wetting their beds. This is obviously not a very impressive field of study, because these are complaints that we tend to laugh at, and, more often than not, they are treated by old wives' remedies rather than by the advice of doctors.

The problems posed by these complaints are by no means petty. Urination, which occasionally is a very difficult function to control even in adults, is the only excretory function existing in the fetus. Urinary incontinence is the oldest of our habits, since it dates back to before we are born. Perhaps this is why this obstinate lack of discipline occasionally persists. Hypnotists have always obtained excellent results with urinary incontinence (78 percent cures and 15.6 percent improvements, according to Cullerre. They have also succeeded in curing even more serious cases of bladder complaints in adults. Dr. R. Chertok reported total recovery of several persons who were afflicted with serious disorders (incontinence, largely increased amounts of urine, retention of or extreme frequency of the need to urinate). Because of this, these people had been unable to lead a normal life and sometimes even felt that their lives were in danger.

The results from hypnosis on adults are very promising, because previously the hypnotists' efforts had been limited to the treatment of children. It is the contraction of the bladder expelling drops of urine into the urethra that causes the need to urinate. As this is a reflex controlled by the spinal cord in an area that is furthest from the cerebrum (the sacral vertebrae), we can understand that in these cases hypnosis is more than mere persuasion or an appeal to the reasoning of the subject. It seems that hypnosis has an influence on the least controllable areas of the individual and on his deepest being.

Warts are a minor complaint. We do not know how they develop or what the contagious conditions are. Nor do we know why they occasionally disappear. Sometimes they resist all treatment; sometimes they disappear simply by suggestion. They are the most minor and insignificant form of skin disease, but they can be influenced by suggestion when electrolysis, cautery, and radiotherapy have failed. Perhaps it is the epidermis, and not the warts, that is involved. Some skin diseases are very difficult to cure, but will disappear as if by magic.

Elliotson reported curing a case of impetigo of two years' duration and another case of long-standing psoriasis. Dr. Hamilton Osgood, who studied hypnotism in Europe and then practiced in Boston at the beginning of this century, cured an eleven-year-old boy who had suffered from eczema since he was eighteen months old. The eczema extended from his umbilicus to his feet; his forearms were covered with crusts and sores; and there were deep inflamed fissures on the wrists and large sores in the armpits. After the first sitting, the irritation ceased. At the end of a month's treatment, all trace of the eczema had disappeared. Although there was some return of it a year later, this yielded to suggestion and complete recovery took place.

Osgood also cured a woman aged sixty-eight who had been suffering from eczema for eight years. There was complete recovery after eighteen sittings, despite the fact that only slight hypnosis was induced and the patient retained full memory of all that was said or done during the sittings.

Bramwell mentioned a particularly difficult case. The patient was a woman, aged forty-nine, suffering from eczema and severe constipation. He attempted to hypnotize her sixty-seven times, but the attempts failed. At the sixty-eighth sitting somnambulism was induced. All the irritation vanished immediately, her constipation disappeared, and after two weeks of treatment all trace of eczema had disappeared.

Eczema poses some strange problems. It can be cured in a patient who is hardly influenced by hypnosis, and it can be very resistant when the subject is not in a somnambulistic state. There are all types of eczema, and its origins, though vague, are situated either in the organism or in the intellect. A psychological portrait of the patient would therefore be necessary before formulating an opinion about proper treatment.

AN EXTRAORDINARY VICTORY

After Dr. A. A. Mason's cure of a case of ichthyosis, or "fish skin" disease, a congenital disease whose first symptoms are sometimes observed in the fetus, hypnotherapy became even more powerful. In this disease the whole body, except for the chest, neck, and face, is covered with blackish scales, which are so brittle that fissures and patterns can develop in the skin. Dr. Mason's patient was fifteen years old. His parents had tried everything, and so had surgeons. The scales had been rubbed off the palms of his hands, and healthy skin had been grafted from his chest. Ten days later, the grafted skin was as dark as the rest of the diseased areas. The doctors tried again, this time going deeper into the palms. The result was worse. The skin graft took, but contracted, resulting in a clawlike hand.

Mason, who was then only twenty-six, recommended suggestive therapy. At the East Grinstead hospital, in a suburb of London, he hypnotized the boy and repeated insistently that his left arm was going to get better. Five days later the scaly coating became soft and peeled off, and the surface of his arm was clean. The photographs included in Mason's work are dated February 15 and 23, 1951. The first photograph shows only a few patches of healthy skin. The second shows a normal arm. After ten days of treatment the arm was cleared from the shoulder to the wrist.

Then the boy's other arm, legs, and body proceeded to clear just as quickly. On February 17 the legs were completely covered with scales. By March 19 there were only a few patches left. The patient was almost entirely cured in just over a month; 70 percent of the affected areas had improved. It was mainly at the patient's extremities—fingers, hands, and feet—that the disease persisted. However, this boy, who had previously had very little social contact because of the ugliness and foul odor of his lesions, could now lead a normal life. His withdrawn, moody nature had changed, and he became pleasant and sociable. This improvement was still obvious four years after hypnotic treatment had been terminated.

Strictly speaking, this was not a cure. But perhaps it was more than a cure—for there was a reversal of the natural course of a diseased condition. However, in his book Mason devoted only a few lines to this treatment, in the chapter on hypnosis and its phenomena, even though at the time it occurred he did give a scientific justification of the case. Mason preferred to consider this case, which definitely carried a lot of weight in Great Britain's official recognition of hypnosis (1955), as an example of psychosomatic medicine. In his discussion on the fact that congenital diseases can be influenced by hypnosis, Mason echoed the *British Medical Journal* by concluding that the present concepts regarding the relationship between the body and the mind have to be revised. He noted that other prodigious cures had occurred, but that not all these could be credited to hypnosis. Some could possibly be attributed to an excitant provoking an intense emotional reaction in the subject, which in turn produced the salutary mental response.

We are already familiar with this modest type of reasoning, for it is the indirect approach taken by all men who are puzzled by the unusual. Charcot (among others) specified the circumstances necessary for miraculous cures to occur. Certain conditions must be assembled (such as mountain, cave, semidarkness, river, smoke, mist) before a powerful excitant can set off an emotional state with equally powerful effects. Some people claim that this emotional state is religious or sentimental, but Charcot considered it hysterical.

Let us assume that under given conditions, the combination "stimulus—intense emotion—spiritual response" is endowed with extraordinary powers and, in particular, a curative power having nothing in common with medical treatments. This can hardly be challenged, even if we do not profess to have any faith in hypnosis. But if we wish to remain objective, we should acknowledge that these emotive factors were not present at the East Grinstead hospital, where the boy with fish skin disease was treated. Furthermore, a "cure" of this type would not have been endorsed by The Lourdes Medical Office, for whom a 70 percent improvement is never sufficient. (The Lourdes Medical Office, which is made up of fifteen doctors, keeps records of miraculous cures. It ascertains, among other things, that there is no medical explanation for the cure and that the cure does not conform to natural laws.)

But we must consider the case in its true proportions: a congenital skin disease did regress 70 percent under hypnotherapy.

AT THE SOURCE OF THE VITAL IMPULSE

Why was the skin of Dr. Mason's young patient covered with scales? Where in the human machine did the orders for this originate? We do not know, but it seems that through hypnosis (and with favorable conditions, which we do not know either), Mason was able to implant a suggestion in the boy's mind and make it travel down to his nerve endings, even reaching those nervous centers that are situated beyond the *human* being at the very core of the *animal* being, and that transmit the orders controlling our organization and growth. Furthermore, this cure was effected on a boy during puberty; that is, during that special period when the internal forces controlling the growth of the individual send more messages and materials for its development than at any subsequent period. Every circuit—in fact, every communications pathway (and we are purposely using these general terms, which are not entirely accurate, so as to include everything, both the lymphatic capillaries and the networks on which Chinese acupuncture is based)—all these pathways are extremely dilated during this active period of puberty.

So it is possible that the thought current (or the nonthinking thought) commanded by the hypnotist is transmitted directly beyond the individual's consciousness to the very essence of his being, to his animal core and to the source of the species. Does it reach those conjectural, problematic centers where the faculty of adaptation is situated? Is this adaptation center itself also subjected to the direction of evolution? Nothing leads us to believe that this is so, but there is nothing to contradict it either.

The skin has the power to adapt spontaneously. Our very existence begins with an adaptation signaled by the skin. The individual, who is bathed in maternal fluids until he is born, actually begins to breathe the moment his epidermis signals that he has entered a different environment.

Since the skin and the nervous system have a common origin, it seems likely that they are closely connected, attending to the evolutionary needs of the species. It is also likely that in certain cases this connection persists, along with an interaction that is possible only if the orders and information relayed are clear and contain no emotional overtones. Thus only would orders reach the innermost being.

We have differentiated the following levels in the individual:

Center	*Nature of action*	*Nature of order*	*Mode of execution*	*Nature of execution*
Cerebral hemispheres	thinks and balances	deliberate	calculated	voluntary
Rest of the nervous system	excites and stimulates	prethought	programmed	automatic
?	fashions	unthinking	spontaneous	organic

The purpose of hypnotherapy is to help inhibit the thinking area so that the first two levels can be bypassed in order to reach the effective level immediately. Thus, intelligence is prevented from intervening and so is its inhibiting action.

It does not matter what name we give to this lowest center: vital impulse, animal nature, "naturizing" nature, etc. Nor does it matter where it is located. This is secondary to the beneficial influence that hypnosis may be able to exert on it.

PROOF THROUGH THE EPIDERMIS

It seems that the skin, whose diseases are sometimes so resistant to treatment and yet whose cures at other times can be so rapid, is controlled by the nature (or innermost being) of the species, not by the intellect, and it is characteristic of this nature to direct itself automatically with force and without deliberation. It is unlike the intellect, which is reflective; which exerts its will only when it has reached a conclusion; which weighs the pros and cons, discriminates, and makes its decision after evaluating the arguments. (And the word "argument" implies that there is an alternate proposition that has been rejected after due consideration.) At this level there is dispersion, hesitation, vagrancy. But the innermost being is a vital impulse and cannot be so wasteful. It has only one goal, which is to keep the species alive and let it develop. It cannot settle for indecision. It is deaf to orders based on reason.

By inhibiting the deliberating brain, deep hypnosis creates a state in which the epidermis and the more decisive levels of the nervous system are again closely connected. It is essential to reestablish this connection. Moreover, it is possible that by doing this a similar influence can be exerted on other organs as well as the skin, but in a different way. In any case, the epidermis appears extremely responsive and obedient when we are able to bypass the intellect and inform it of our wishes in terms that it can comprehend. This, at least, is what hypnotists seem to have proved in the past three-quarters of a century.

From the above remarks, however, we certainly must not conclude that hypnosis always manages to mobilize the innermost being of the individual. As we have already seen, slight hypnosis is often sufficient to obtain salutary results, but hypnosis in the intermediary stages does not automatically become efficacious in these innermost depths. Assistance from the upper segments of the brain can still be necessary.

For example, Dr. Hamilton Osgood reported one very difficult case. A young woman, aged twenty-eight, was suffering from *eczema rubrum* affecting the scalp, face, hands, and feet. This condition had been unrelieved by four years' careful treatment. The palms of her hands were so thickened and intersected by deep fissures that the condition almost resembled elephantiasis. Hypnosis was induced at the first sitting, but it took forty-six more sittings before all trace of the disease had disappeared.

This cure had to be effected quite differently from the one effected on the boy during puberty. Perhaps this woman's eczema was caused by some inner conflict or by a personality problem that was disturbing her brain. Self-punishment, self-protection against some unknown attack, self-destruction of initiative—these are points of conscience that the subject does not even admit to himself; but they have been revealed through psychoanalysis. This was not known in Osgood's time because Freud was then only beginning his work. In their ignorance, hypnotists had no idea that curing the external disease could aggravate the internal disorder that had provoked this external disease and consequently cause an even more formidable neurosis in its place.

Psychoanalysis, psychology, and substitution neurosis all deal with the so-called upper level of the individual, in the intellect where thoughts are formed. But studies have shown how dependent various functions are on the autonomic nervous system. Even though these functions are regulated by various centers, we still acknowledge the *intellectual* priority of the cerebral lobes.

So it becomes tempting and convenient to make this simple classification. At the highest level, there is consciousness. At the lowest, there is the vital impulse, the being that wants to live and last unreservedly. It does not function blindly, but rather savagely as a whole, and like a plant, with the same intensity and the same lack of hesitation.

THE PERCEPTIVE COMPLEX OF THE INNER BEING

This "inner being," which we have placed at the lowest level because this is the position that it theoretically occupies, is very well equipped. It has its own nervous system (the autonomic) and its own organ for perception (the skin), and these are sufficient to ensure its smooth functioning when this is only a matter of living and adjusting to the environment.

But, in addition to this inner being, there is the individual himself, who has to be informed in order to find his food and reproduce. The senses are responsible for this ability to relate to the outside world.

Just as plants put forth flowers to attract fertilizing insects and thus ensure their reproduction, so animals are equipped to investigate and exploit their surroundings. In some animals—for example, man—one segment of the nervous system, namely the brain, is highly developed. Hearing, seeing, and smelling are meaningless unless these sensations are properly identified and interpreted by the brain. The cerebral centers that interpret this information from the senses have grown more complex and now form a unit (or a "dispatching center" as it is called today) that is perfectly equipped to collect, understand, and act upon the information relayed to it.

This dispatching center performs its task so vigorously that it is easy for us to believe it is the master control. The vegetative being has obligingly provided the cerebrum with the necessary organs for comprehension and movement and equipped them with their own sensory perceptors, which are situated in the dermis, so as to give this dispatching center a more accurate perception of the things with which the body comes into contact.

Has the vegetative being handed over its control of these organs to the dispatching center? This seems unlikely, but we could be mistaken—and we hope we are. Descartes obviously believed it had: *Cogito ergo sum,* he declared, "I think, therefore I am." But Nietzsche did not accept this reasoning: "The deceptive magic of words! . . . a series of risky propositions, whose foundation is difficult to prove," he observed. The Cartesian premise, which is contested by philosophers, is even more contested by physiologists. It is surprising that between the two mechanisms, one characterized by erratic thought, hesitations, and uncertainties, and the other by automatic, almost instantaneous responses that bewilder us by their precision, we concede the role of master control to the former mechanism, the thinking processes.

Pavlov wrote that the supreme role of ordering and distributing all the organism's activities is played by the cerebral hemispheres. This would certainly be very practical, because we believe we comprehend the cerebral hemispheres and feel that they are responsible for our whole functioning. All we would have to do is establish how they work (and we have been trying to do this for two centuries) so as to have the key that opens every door. But the matter is not so simple. Everything that our senses are concerned with and everything resulting from conscious acts are controlled by the inner being, which has not handed over its controls. But there are intermediary elements between the summit (consciousness) and the vegetative being (which is the materialization of the vital impulse. Between the cerebral lobes, which control our sensory experiences, and the visceral system, whose activity is not controlled by our will, there is a whole sector that is of the utmost importance and whose role is both complex and confusing. It acts as a liaison unit, a filter, and a regulator. It seems that nothing escapes it and that everything passes through it, with the result that consciousness (cerebral) influences the entire organism and visceral fluids affect consciousness through chemical reactions set off by hormones. In turn, hormones are secreted by glands, over which we have no control.

THE COMPLEXITIES OF THE BRAIN

It seems that hypnotic action can be exerted on both the cerebral and visceral levels and can influence either the manifestations of the vital impulse, which are connected to the autonomic nervous system, or the thought processes occurring in the cerebral hemispheres. The cerebral level is less subtle but much more complex than the other level. On the one hand, it is continually calculating, reckoning, and ordering acts on the basis of data that has been pre-evaluated. On the other hand, the series of reflections, or chain reflexes from which the action results, can take all sorts of meandering paths, following intentions that are difficult to fathom. If a main road is blocked, there might be ten collateral paths leading to the desired spot. And so in diseases involving the cerebral hemispheres (where there is no lesion, of course) there can be no *definite* recovery until the maze of recognized motives and unavowed intentions has been straightened out.

This is the principal goal of psychoanalysis, and it is very valuable to the hypnotist, who otherwise risks obtaining only temporary, unstable, and even dangerous results. This is because his therapy may erase a symptom but will have no bearing on the psychological conflict that caused it and that may create other disorders.

This risk is present in the majority of diseases. Previously clinicians were wary about suppressing ailments as commonplace as rheumatism, gout, and eczema. Cutting the disease short is dangerous (although all therapies treating symptoms run this danger ninety times out of a hundred). We must not believe that by disclosing the "psychogenic" origin of the phenomenon being treated we are insuring ourselves against this risk. If we question subjects long enough, they will all find some conflict, some suppressed desire or repressed grievance, some reason for self-punishment, self-protection, or self-revolt that could be considered important. However, although strict Freudian psychoanalysts watch out for this, a psychoanalyst who is willing to resort to hypnosis can accelerate his investigation of the subconscious considerably, because the use of suggestion allows him to take shortcuts that cannot be used when the subject's intellect retains all its critical senses.

Most of the successful treatments effected by hypnosis, such as those recorded by Hirschfass and Schultz, are today attributed to psychosomatic medicine. The successes due strictly to hypnosis are considered either remote, exceptional, or both. But hypnosis, a pioneering science, is already directing its investigations elsewhere.

CHAPTER IX

Triumphs Over Pain

NEARLY everything written about pain becomes rapidly outdated. Research in this field never stops seeking both the areas where the pain is centered and methods of relieving it.

If a patient's pain is intense and cannot be relieved by any of the sedative, anesthesic, hypnotic, or analgesic drugs available, then the surgeon can cut the communication between the painful area and the nervous centers perceiving the sensation. According to the nature of the pain, he can cut the terminal nerve-ending or the root of the nerve; he can destroy the ganglion; or, going even deeper, he can cut the spine itself from the relays connected to it.

If this does not work and the patient continues to suffer intense pain, it can be appeased by isolating the related area of the brain from the rest of the nervous system. This does not remove the cause of the suffering, but the patient will now suffer only passively. He becomes indifferent to his pain, but he also becomes indifferent to many things of a moral, social, or artistic nature, because this reduction of sensitivity also affects the personality.

We shall not go into detail about these various operations, or even describe the network of nerves transmitting pain. We shall simply point out that there is a distinction between the levels of the nervous system. For example, in the face, painful sensations are transmitted by the trigeminal nerve. This nerve, attached to the inferior face of the cerebrum, is the facial nerve and is responsible for headaches. The meninges also owe their sensitivity to this nerve. In the body, painful sensations are transmitted by the spinal nerves going directly into the spinal cord.

In spite of this division between body and mind, there can be no pain unless it is interpreted through the cerebrum, since suffering is relayed through the highest thought levels into the body.

ANESTHESIA BY HYPNOSIS

The following account will help illustrate the great complexity of a problem that had been beyond man's powers until Mesmer. Before him, various means were used to try and stupefy a patient, but these means were not really recommended, since it was believed that pain was salutary because it made the patient repent and thus all would end well. Mesmer noticed only incidentally that magnetism could provide relief. In his *Aphorisms,* published in 1785, he wrote, "Pains, called symptomatic symptoms, yielding to the touch, can be alleviated even though this alleviation does not act on the cause of the disease . . ." (Aphorism 288). This property was overlooked until 1795 when Sir Humphry Davy, the chemist who discovered potassium and sodium, showed that nitrous oxide, or "laughing gas" as it came to be called, could be used in surgery.

At first, animal magnetism maintained its lead over chemical anesthesia. In January 1821 at the Hotel Dieu in Paris, Recamier applied moxas to two subjects who had been magnetized by Dupotet. In 1829, Cloquet surgically removed the cancerous breast of a young woman, who was lucid but insensitive to the pain. In 1820 a young English doctor, Hickmann, anesthetized animals with laughing gas and carbon dioxide. But in the face of general indifference, he committed suicide.

In 1845, James Esdaile began his famous series of operations at Calcutta. His success was so great (only a 5 percent mortality rate) that nobody in India could have any doubts about mesmerism's triumph over pain. Before Esdaile's arrival, some patients were so afraid of being operated on that they had preferred to live with tumors, which were sometimes almost as large as their bodies (the largest weighed eighty pounds). Es-

A Buddhist priest walking on fire
Holmès-Lebel

daile's first patients were convicts and peasants. Later, when the government opened a large hospital for him, he acquired a well-to-do clientele. Denying Esdaile's success (or attributing it to simulation or hysteria) would have been like declaring that day was night. The triumph was absolute and the experiment conclusive: magnetism was a valuable tool for the surgeon who wanted to operate without making his patient suffer pain.

CHEMICAL ANESTHESIA

In 1844 an American dentist, Horace Wells, was the first to use nitrous oxide for surgical anesthesia. Another dentist, Morton, had effected the first anesthesia with ether at Boston in 1846 before an admiring public. A doctor in Georgia had experimented surgically with ether four years earlier. And as far back as 1847, the possibilities of chloroform were being demonstrated in France and England.

Magnetism was overshadowed. Its opponents were only too

happy to deny its undeniable power as an anesthetic. Esdaile sent an indignant protest when the United States Senate offered a prize of $100,000 to the inventor of painless surgery and hesitated between granting it to the discoverers of the anesthetic powers of ether and those of nitrous oxide. Esdaile did not want the reward, but he wanted magnetism to receive the credit it deserved. Yet, in spite of Esdaile's wonders, chemical anesthesia was considered the only safe and practical method of anesthesia.

This opinion has not changed. We continue to administer toxic products to humans by inhalation, inoculation, and perfusion without really knowing at what point these modifications of chemical balance cause repercussions in the organism.

WHERE HYPNOSIS IS STILL INDICATED

Hypnosis still has certain advantages. Here is a significant account, taken from an article by A. A. Mason that appeared in the English journal *Anaesthesia* in June 1955.

A young girl, age twenty-four, perfectly well-balanced and normal, was afflicted with hypertrophy of the breasts. Not only was this very distressing to her, but it had also caused inflammations at various parts of her body. Her doctors decided to operate using regular methods of chemical anesthesia. But during the operation, after the surgeon had removed a large amount of tissue, he was forced to admit that plastic surgery could not be performed right away.

The operation had lasted two and a half hours, and five different anesthesias had been administered. The postoperative events were stormy. The girl became delirious and wanted to get up, she could not stop vomiting, unwound her bandages, lost about three pints of blood, and broke most of her stitches. She left the hospital one month later in a very anemic condition.

When she learned that a second operation would be necessary, she claimed that the mere thought of the previous anesthesia terrified her and asked if she could be given only local anesthesia. But this was not advisable, because large incisions had to be made and it would be a long operation. So the doctors fell back on hypnosis. After three ten-minute sittings, it was obvious that the girl was an excellent subject, able to be put into a very advanced degree of insensibility. As she also had to have two impacted wisdom teeth extracted, her doctors decided to extract these teeth under hypnosis as a trial attempt. The experiment was successful even though it was necessary to use a surgical burr to incise the gum and free one tooth from the maxilla.

When it was time for the breast operation, the patient came to the hospital the night before, slept very well, ate a normal breakfast at eight o'clock, and went to the operating room at ten o'clock without the slightest apprehension.

A pin-pricking test before hypnosis revealed that the whole breast was sensitive with the exception of two cicatricial marks. The hypnotist then proceeded to induce her. He told her that from the neck to the base of the sternum, her whole chest, down to her ribs, was going to become numb and insensitive to pain. Another pin-prick test soon confirmed that this result had been obtained. But in spite of this numbness, the young girl could still feel the coolness of the alcohol the surgeon was freely applying to her chest—in fact, so freely that a drop went into her eye. She made a face and said, "My eye is watering!"

The nurse wiped away this tear while the doctor started to make the incision. The operation was unprecedented. It lasted seventy minutes. Lucid and unconcerned throughout the entire procedure, and without flinching or moving, the girl often spoke and even joked. "Am I thick-skinned?" she asked. After half an hour, she asked for something to drink and drank calmly. Once she signaled that she had just felt a prick. And, in fact, the surgeon had gone beyond the area in the ribs that had been anesthetized by suggestion. Then her hypnotist made sure that the numbness extended from side to side. This was the only incident.

When the operation was over, the patient remarked, "Well done!" She was then asked to sit, as this made the bandaging easier. She obeyed without being assisted by anyone. Then, after the hypnotist told her that she would have no postoperative pain, she was awakened. She smiled, admitted that she had not felt a thing and could not remember anything. Five days later, she left the hospital.

In drawing his conclusions from this experiment, A. A. Mason emphasized the patient's lucidity and the fact that her reflexes continued to protect her. Her awareness of the cold sensation when her chest was being rubbed and of the drop of alcohol in her eye, which she felt immediately, show that many accidents occurring on the operating table, especially the frequent cases of burns, could be avoided. In addition, it is also very important to preserve the coughing reflex, because most deaths under anesthesia are caused by blood, saliva, or vomit entering the respiratory tract. Mason wrote that whenever a patient has to be anesthetized several times, hypnosis is advisable. For example, in patients who are suffering from burns, because they are so difficult to bandage and it is not recommended to anesthetize them often; in orthopedics, where operations have to be repeated; in thoracic or abdominal tapping; and finally for any subject who is afraid or who is in poor physical condition.

There are many other indications for hypnosis in cases where chemical anesthesia is not advisable. We must not forget that hypnosis reduces or even suppresses postoperative shock and that it eliminates postoperative reactions and pain. During surgery, it also allows the patient to drink, thus maintaining his fluid balance.

Unfortunately, under the conditions that it is normally practiced, surgical hypnosis is realizable with only 25 percent of subjects, and this proportion is even less for those undergoing major operations. If surgery is required urgently, hypnosis cannot be used because we cannot know in advance if the subject is hypnotizable and how long it will take to put him in a state of trance suitable for surgery. Chemical anesthetics, which are 100 percent reliable, will always occupy first place.

On the other hand, for those who are able to resort to it, hypnosis does seem to be the ideal method of anesthesia. As preparation for possible future surgery, every cardiac patient should be tested by a practitioner using hypnotic techniques to find out whether he is capable of being induced into a state of trance, thus making chemical anesthesia unnecessary. Regrettably, such experiments are rarely made.

This is even more unfortunate because as hypnotic techniques are perfected, the statistical level of their successes increases accordingly. We would hope that the number of practitioners will increase rapidly.

DENTAL ANESTHESIA

We have already emphasized how necessary it is for hypnosis to remain strictly medical. This restriction does not apply to dentistry, which in its limited field is also medical, since it treats local infections as much as it repairs damage. In addition to great manual dexterity, a dentist requires extensive knowledge and a lot of perspicacity and tact. This is reason enough for the dentist to practice hypnotism, because hypnotism demands these qualities. It is even probable that he will be all the more qualified to hypnotize because he is familiar with problems of a psychological nature. For the dentist, treating patients would be easy if he first did not have to persuade them to let themselves be treated. Convincing, persuading, suggesting, these are the stepping stones to hypnosis.

The applications of hypnosis in dentistry are quite clear. We saw how Dr. Mason's young patient, in a deep trance and without any pain, endured the extraction of a large tooth whose curving roots had made it virtually attached to the maxilla. In addition, the experiment also showed that "glove" anesthesia, which occurs in the moderate trance, is very easily transferred to the mouth or, in particular, to the tooth that is being treated. "Your hand has gone to sleep . . . You did not feel the pin prick . . . now it's your tooth, this tooth, which is becoming numb and insensitive . . ." If the instructions are given precisely enough (and the hypnotist can never be too precise), the procedure can be performed rapidly and without difficulty. And lastly, the hypnotized patient will obey the suggestion not to salivate and, if necessary, not to bleed.

There are some drawbacks, however. The first is that, as in all cases involving loss of consciousness, the presence of a third party is necessary. We do not want a dishonest subject accusing the hypnotist of having taken advantage of him while he was unconscious. The second drawback is due to some of the uncertainties of hypnosis and to the fact that the preparation and induction can take a long time. With good subjects, this time gets shorter at every sitting, thanks to the subject's training and to the posthypnotic suggestion that he fall asleep promptly the next time. In time, only a few moments have to be devoted to the induction procedure. With difficult or stubborn patients, it is better to give up immediately.

Hypnosis is not essential for relieving pain; the regular analgesics work well and are easy to administer. But if the patient is suffering from a disease or allergy that makes chemical anesthesia dangerous or painful, then hypnosis is indicated. It can be used in association with a "topical" anesthetic, a substance that anesthetizes superficially without spreading deep into the tissues.

In short, the moderate trance, which can be induced in about 30 percent of subjects, permits superficial procedures, and in the deep trance, which is not as easily induced (25 to 30 percent of subjects), extractions, deep drilling, grinding, etc. can be performed. Nor should we forget the importance of the slight trance. Its phenomena are not always very obvious. Nevertheless, it works inconspicuously but surely: 85 to 90 percent of subjects succumb to it provided they are willing.

We shall quote these thoughts by M. R. Meadel about the advantages of this almost general suggestibility:

> In current practice, only *sleeping thresholds, hypnoidal thresholds and maximum light sleep* can be of interest to us. According to suggestibility percentages, it seems that a large number of successes are within our reach. If we work on the principle that *the sensitivity threshold increases as the sleep becomes deeper and that the subject's suggestibility becomes greater* as his state of relaxation and somnolence asserts itself, then the first two stages of hypnosis are sufficient to create a conditioned state yielding the desired results.
>
> In fact, if it is proper for psychiatrists and neuro-psychiatrists to pursue investigation of a psycho-physiological nature with the aim of curative treatments, then it is proper for us to investigate two factors which are essential to us as dentists: analgesia with muscular relaxation; the suppression of apprehension.
>
> It is one of our great ambitions to have patients who can come to us relaxed, consult us with absolutely no fears and who, consequently, will be able to regard more lightly the nervous shocks that we subject them to.
>
> It would certainly be pleasant for us to be able to treat in-

sensitized patients with a minimum of nervous and physical expenditure.

These few lines cover all that must be said about the enormous advantages available to the dentist who is willing to use slight hypnosis wherever possible and as often as necessary, that is to say, very often.

PRIOR CONDITIONING

There are a great many men and women for whom the waiting room, the dentist's chair, the whining of the drill, and even the smell of pharmaceutical products constitute signals setting off a conditioned defense reflex and a hostile stiffening of the body, which is almost insurmountable because of this very conditioning. A hypnotic approach can dispel their fears.

M. R. Meadel, inspired by certain English hypnotists, made a means of conditioning, or rather reconditioning (since it consists of replacing undesirable reflexes with desirable ones), available to his colleagues in the form of a recording that prepared the subject. Originally, Meadel had planned that the subject should listen to it in his own home, several times if necessary, so that the conditioning would be completed by the time he arrived at the dentist's office. Occasionally a mild sedative completed the action. But this patient education needs to be guided, and many practitioners prefer a recording that is played in their office, thus leading directly in to the dental work itself.

The record has two parts: first, what the author called "the gymnastics of general muscular relaxation," which is a synthesis of muscular relaxation as obtained in general anesthesia or a deep hypnotic sleep; and a series of strong but gradual suggestions ending with desensitivity in the area to be treated.

The dentist then repeats the same suggestions in the same continuous and monotonous tone as the recording, thus creating a conditioned reflex associated with muscular relaxation. By posthypnotic suggestion, he will suppress the patient's fears so that in the future he will come back calm and relaxed. When in the dentist's chair, he may then display an almost automatic relaxation of all his muscles. Posthypnotic suggestion will have prepared him to put himself in this state by himself, at a simple signal that the practitioner established during the first sitting. While the patient is in a hypnotic state, there should be nothing different from the treatment he would receive in his waking state.

In addition to making the work easier, suggestion offers the dentist many other advantages: for example, holes left by the extraction of teeth heal more rapidly, both by an accelerated process of natural tissue repair and because the subject can be told not to suck or lick the wound. Suggestion can help a patient having a difficult time adjusting to a dental prosthesis. If there is a difficulty stemming from the subject's grinding his teeth in his sleep, this can possibly be avoided by suggesting to him that he remain alert to this sound while he is asleep. If this is a very old habit, however, hypnosis may not be so successful because the idiosyncrasy may be the result of some abnormality that would have to be explained.

Children are more difficult to treat than adults if they already have had a bad experience at the dentist's. Hypnosis will help to stem their fears, but it will be an arduous process. If, on the other hand, they have no prejudices against dentists, the dentist can take advantage of their favorable disposition and gain their confidence. Dawson Watts and Moss, British specialists, believe that children under twelve do not have a sufficient span of attention to be hypnotized by fixed gazing or to relax by the usual methods, so they advise using more indirect methods. One of these, advocated by Moss, consists in asking the child to close his eyes and relive a film or a television series that he liked and then, when he has a clear picture before his eyes, to raise his arm. If the child obeys this suggestion, the practitioner knows that he can direct the child to perform another suggested movement, while all the time insisting on the drowsiness caused by the mental picture which the child must not stop looking at, even though he is feeling so sleepy.

The habit of thumb sucking affects dental hygiene by deforming the palate and the teeth. By reasoning with the child under hypnosis, this habit can be gradually reduced in 80 percent of cases, unless it corresponds to a psychological state that only a pediatrician specializing in psychiatry could perceive.

Children pose special problems in dentistry. It seems that the rapport is not as important with children as it is with adults.

In adults, when the dentist is competent the rapport is easily established on a basis of confidence and cordiality (or deference, if cordiality is not in order). Consequently, even if he remains extremely attentive to his relationships with his patients, and even if he puts a maximum of interest and psychology into these rapports, the hypnodentist still has a great deal of mental freedom in the practice of his profession. This provides him with an opportunity to observe things for which a doctor does not have time.

The problems that must be resolved by the dentist are relatively simple. The treatment is usually stereotyped and necessitates several pauses. But the time a doctor must devote to studying a case, making a diagnosis, and then treating it, the dentist can use to study his patient's reactions. So it is possible that the dental profession could contribute significantly to furthering our knowledge of hypnosis—and it has helped considerably in clarifying this knowledge in the past thirty years in the United States and Great Britain. As a result of recent legislation in England, dentists and doctors, only, are entitled to practice hypnotism, which is a domain reserved for the licensed medical specialties, like anesthesiology and obstetrics.

Hypnodentists in the United States are trying to obtain similar rights. And they deserve to obtain them. It was in the United States that the systematic application of hypnosis in dentistry was first advocated. Back in 1925 Thomas Burgess, a psychology teacher at Concordia College in Minnesota, gave tremendous impetus to the use of hypnosis. As he himself was not a dentist, he was able to show with complete disinterest how easy it is for a dentist to help prepare a pregnant woman for a painless delivery of her child. This is, in fact, extremely simple, because once desensitivity has been obtained in the mouth, it is very easy to transfer it to the pelvic region. The obstetrician should be introduced to the future patient under hypnosis, and thus a rapport that can only be advantageous for her delivery is established.

FEAR OF CHILDBIRTH

If there is any natural function that man has utterly falsified and even perverted by his "intelligence," it is reproduction. Childbirth should be effected without any complications. Animals prove this every day: a brief retreat, a few hours' labor, a little discomfort, then the young are born and the mother is well again by the next day.

Why is it so different with humans? It is because the intellect intervenes. Our distant ancestors did not understand the relationship between conception and birth, and the swelling of the woman's abdomen followed by the arrival of the child seemed mysterious to them. They were afraid of everything they could not explain, and this phenomenon must have been all the more terrifying because occasionally the mother died.

And so the fear of childbirth originated. Apprehensions were passed down from generation to generation, as were the stories of women who died while giving birth.

Medicine, when it developed, was not a great help. It did not alleviate the pain, and sometimes it even increased the danger. When civilization created maternity hospitals, there were often terrible risks of infection to mothers. In the absence of prophylaxis and even basic hygienic measures, puerperal fever claimed alarming numbers of mothers, until Semmelweis discovered the reason for it. And finally aseptic procedures were enforced.

With aseptic procedures, the mortality rate decreased and attention could be given to combating the pain involved in childbirth. Attempts were made to alleviate the pain by methods introduced with chemical anesthesia. In 1853, Queen Victoria of England was the first woman to give birth to a child under chloroform. She inhaled it through a handkerchief. Even today, giving "twilight sleep" means inducing a light state of anesthesia.

But putting the patient to sleep in this way, regardless of the method or the product, has certain disadvantages. The obstetrician's task is not facilitated if the woman is asleep. Furthermore, until the umbilical cord is cut, the child absorbs gaseous products carried in the mother's blood. Local anesthesia is almost inconvenient: it interferes with the action of organs whose functioning is most necessary.

The ideal solution is not to suppress the pain as much as to reduce the extent of it and reassure the woman. If we can erase her fears, this would be helpful from a physiological point of view. Theories of painless childbirth were only recently accepted, when the scruples of those who took the words of the Bible literally were disregarded: "In sorrow, thou shalt bring forth children." The idea that hypnosis can facilitate childbirth is not new. Dumontpellier and Mesnet at the Hôtel-Dieu and Pritz in Vienna were experimenting with it around 1815.

Under present conditions, it is obvious that hypnosis alone is not the ideal solution. Local anesthesia is not the answer. Suppressing fear does not necessarily suppress the contractions, which are provoked by it and which still persist like conditioned reflexes. Moreover, there is no process, hypnotic or otherwise, that can make a subject perform a complex action like childbirth at the first attempt and without experience, because it can be adequately accomplished only with reasonable education (either of the individual or of the reflexes).

There is a technique for everything. Childbirth, however natural it may be, is learned. In the last century there was scarcely any gathering of people where childbirth could be freely discussed. Ignorance prevailed. In spite of the experience of midwives and obstetricians, the circumstances surrounding birth were only summarily known. More progress must have been made on the day doctors were able to study the uterus of a woman in labor with X-rays than in the previous two thousand years.

It was only just after World War I that we began examining scientifically the role of the woman in labor, a procedure in which she has the central role. Some doctors boldly declared that childbirth should be approached like a sporting activity: the participant should be trained so that her physical condition will be the best possible and her actions as well coordinated as possible.

At first, it was insisted that an abdominal girdle was necessary for the future mother to help her retain her body shape and protect her from injury. Then, she was carefully taught how to perform the required movements at the right moment. It was later noted, however, that the required movements were limited to the pelvic region and that simultaneous other movements, resulting from a lack of self-control, hindered rather than helped the most important movements, that is, those performed spontaneously by the uterus. Consequently, doctors believed it was very important for the woman to relax all her muscles as much as she could so as to aid this natural labor. Finally, it was discovered that when the woman was bearing down, the pressures exerted by the diaphragm influenced her respiration and that this, in turn, could impede the expulsive action of the uterus. So women had to learn how to control their respiration too.

This education made women familiar with the idea of childbirth. They would no longer have to go into labor helpless, but would be able to provide educated cooperation. This in itself made the procedure much less frightening. The old fears were being dispelled.

At last, with the old prejudices cleared away, the field was open again to hypnosis. In addition to improvements of a mechanical nature (such as controlled breathing, toned-up muscles, deliberate bearing down) and intellectual advances (optimism, confidence, cooperation, familiarization with places and people), hypnosis could offer two advantages: precisely localized anesthesia that would not interfere with controlled movements and general or partial amnesia, which would erase the memory of any pain that it would be beneficial to forget.

"PAINLESS" CHILDBIRTH

Both these advantages of hypnosis cannot be the lot of all women. Suggestibility, which permits us to induce a deep trance and cause amnesia on waking works in only one out of four women, and local insensitivity can be attained in about one out of three. Therefore, in formulating methods of "painless" childbirth, we are not able to take maximum suggestibility as the basis. Most of these methods have resulted in a procedure that is much more painful than it would be under deep hypnosis.

Today, the various Russian, English, American, and French methods tend to have a similar preparation. This begins around the seventh month, but it is often preceded by instructions on making the entire pregnancy easier. Generally, doctors initiate conditioning (the future mother is taught movements that must occur with almost reflexive spontaneity) and unconditioning (since all the old reflexes of panic and fear must be erased). This is the same sort of double process already being utilized in dental offices.

In the U.S.S.R., where the psychophysical method of preparation, developed by Velvolski in 1921, is currently used, the vast majority of childbirths are painless. In England, Read's "natural" method is widely used. Neither method is dependent on suggestion. Read tries to suppress the "apprehension-contraction-pain" syndrome, while the Russians depend on conditioned reflexes. Nevertheless, in both countries, as well as in many others, it is considered helpful if the subject is also willing to undergo hypnosis, and occasionally slight doses of an analgesic are given too. In 1954, following some eight thousand observations, Velvolski published the results from his method combining hypnotic analgesia and practices based on Pavlov's theories. This new method, derived from hypnotism, is called a "psychoprophylactic" method.

In addition to the precautions that must be taken whenever someone is hypnotized, we must not lead the woman to believe that hypnosis dispenses her from that personal effort that plays a large part in the alleviation of her pain. She must realize the necessity of giving her full cooperation to those assisting her in the delivery, even if the hypnotist is not present. We must ask her to be passive, but this is easily obtained in a hypnotized subject. She must also be instructed about the different stages of the delivery and the various reactions that should accompany these stages, whether the birth is "natural" or "conditioned." This principle, that the woman in labor should rely primarily on herself, means that the hypnotist should not resort to domination techniques when inducing hypnosis in her. For this same reason, during the preparatory hypnotic sittings when the rapport is being established, the patient should not feel that someone else's will can be imposed upon her own. Relaxation, drowsiness, and partial amnesia throughout the entire period of labor (but not at the terminal stage, because it is good for the mother to be aware of the birth of her child) are the main goals, as well as anesthesia of the painful regions. Naturally, if a deep trance can be induced in the patient, these goals will be attained and the woman will play an active role in the delivery without awakening. With this type of patient, it is useful to instill a posthypnotic suggestion during the preparatory sittings. The hypnotist might suggest that she put herself into a hypnotic state at a given signal, for example, at her first labor pains. Thus, the only deliveries completely free of pain are those in which hypnosis is superimposed on the training the patient has received.

There is still more progress to be made, that is obvious. The woman must be even more informed and better trained. She must be completely experienced in the actions necessary on her part during delivery. Above all, the techniques for obtaining deep hypnosis must be perfected so that all women, and not just one quarter of them, can benefit from it.

It will be difficult to attain these goals through controlled hypnosis, which preserves an occasional state of consciousness. It is better if the dissociation is neither integral nor permanent. We do not want robot-like deliveries. Mental absence of the mother is undesirable because the boundary between ignorance and indifference is slight. However, the fractionation method of inducing hypnosis can be used successfully because it permits us to take advantage of the patient's lucid moments, the length of which is determined by the circumstances.

CHAPTER X

Is the Personality in Danger?

SINCE hypnosis is characterized by suggestibility, which, at its most effective, results in absolute domination by the hypnotist, it is often feared that the subject's personality can be affected and that he can be placed at the hypnotist's mercy permanently.

This is often the main reason people give for not letting themselves be hypnotized. At the end of the last century, many people felt that the subject was nothing more than a puppet. For example, in demonstrations of hypnotism girls of fine character were made to play the role of murderesses quietly killing all the victims placed before them, and heads of families were made to leave exorbitant amounts of money for their doctors or to give it to an accomplice appointed by them. Certainly, the murdered victims were able to get back on their feet and shake the dust off themselves. The flabbergasted fathers would rip up the checks that would have been their ruination. But the spectators were not convinced. They reasoned that thousands of susceptible people could commit such criminal acts if a demoniacal hypnotist took it into his head to take advantage of them.

Once in a while, news reports confirmed this impression. Some young girls let themselves be raped (the Castellau case, Var assizes, 1865; the Lévy case at Rouen, 1878). One rich woman handed over all her jewelry to a man she met on a train. Some female patients were intimately attended by their doctors and only learned the depth of the examination when they were dressed again. Mesnet related several examples like this in a medico-legal study entitled *Acts of Indecency, Violations of*

Women's Sexual Organs in Provoked Somnambulism and Fascination (1894). Mesnet had no doubt that a hypnotized woman in a deep trance could be violated and that more often than not, she would not defend herself. But she would not remember anything on awakening.

Although Mesnet was conducting his experiments at the Hôtel-Dieu in Paris, his opinion on this matter coincided with that of the Nancy school. But the Salpêtrière hypnotists were not so sure. Gilles de la Tourette maintained that rape would be possible only if the subject were reduced to a state in which her body was actionless and reactionless. There would be no risk, however, prior to this lethargic state, because hypnosis makes a woman strong enough to repel all assaults. The Salpêtrière studies were made on hysterical patients who were involuntary but constant simulators and whose behavior was almost always unpredictable.

The law seems to agree with Mesnet. It recognizes that a person can commit a crime under hypnosis. In both cases of rape mentioned above, the defendants were found guilty. But we shall never know if the victims were at that final stage of lethargic helplessness referred to by Gilles de la Tourette, or if they were in a somnambulistic state where they could have struggled if, unconsciously, they had not been somewhat willing,

The last time that hypnosis was featured in a trial in France that stirred worldwide interest was the "Gouffé's trunk" case, which was heatedly discussed for two years On December 16, 1890, Michel Eyraud and Gabrielle Bompard faced charges before the Seine assizes of murdering the bailiff Gouffé, who was strangled or hung with a belt. Gabrielle was said to have passed the belt around his neck "for fun" while Gouffé was courting her. Henri Robert, who was defending Gabrielle, contended that she had acted against her own will under hypnosis. He quoted the theories of the Nancy school and made Professor Liégeois, one of Bernheim's associates, appear before the court to testify that a hypnotized subject is nothing more "than a pure automaton."

Brouardel, the court's consultant, who had examined the young girl, maintained that she was in full possession of her judgment and that, furthermore, Liégeois, as a law professor, was not qualified to gives testimony about hypnosis.

The jury remained puzzled, and because of another, very different question (about the very nature of the crime), Gabrielle was not condemned to death.

Since then, our law courts have rarely been confronted with a defense claiming hypnotic influence, perhaps because there are now very few fathers who would believe their daughters had been hypnotized by their seducers. Or perhaps it is because no public prosecutor finds a complaint like this acceptable. Since according to some, hypnotism does not exist, it would be like accusing a ghost or a werewolf! (In his manual of psychiatry, published in 1925, Roques de Fursac commented on a Berlin court case in which the jury found a hypnotist guilty of raping a young woman while she was in a trance: "In legal medicine, hypnosis does not exist.")

WHEN MORAL BARRIERS FALL

How does one decide between truth and delusion? Can a subject be led to perform acts that are morally wrong and that he would not perform in his normal waking state?

For a long time hypnotists have been aware of a powerful "moral barrier" that makes the subject suddenly rebel. At Salpêtrière, no matter how suggestible a female subject was, she would refuse to take off her clothes as though preparing for a bath, or refuse to pour a bottle of ink over her new dress. We are certain that, generally speaking, there is an alertness persisting at the back of the hypnotized subject's mind. However, it has not been proved that this exists in the final stage of hypnosis. It has been demonstrated that this self-control can be suppressed. Taking the necessary precautions, hypnotists have been able to make subjects attempt to seize poisonous rattlesnakes. Other hypnotized subjects have thrown acid at the faces of innocent people (who were protected by a sheet of nonreflecting glass). But it is difficult to guarantee that the subjects would not have done the same in their waking state. They could perform destructive actions under hypnosis either because they knew that the experimenter would never let a catastrophe occur, or because it did not really matter to them if one did occur: they would not really be responsible for it.

On the other hand, by using an indirect, circuitous approach, some subjects can be led into any crime without it even being necessary to hypnotize them. For subjects with weak or excitable natures, the crime merely has to be depicted as an exploit, a feat of arms, or a liberation; he must see the crime from a meritorious point of view with no stigma attached to it by public morality and convention.

The hypnotist employing this power of illusion along with hypnosis should produce considerable, if not unlimited, results from a subject. With a good knowledge of the individual, he can suppress the subject's critical judgment; the range of lies that can be reinforced by hallucinations and the limits to what a subject in a somnambulistic trance will accept are almost boundless. However, the form and nature of the rapport must be kept in mind, because this rapport gives the hypnotist a privileged role and a special, clearly defined prestige. Throughout the entire sitting, the hypnotist imposes his actions, asserts his power, and demands that attention be paid exclusively to his words. So how does he make a woman undress as though he were not there, when he keeps insisting on his presence. If she does undress, we have to ask ourselves why she is willing to undress in front of this overbearing man who is neither her lover nor her doctor.

Inversely, when a hysterical patient who has come to consult her doctor about a vaginal infection falls into a trance almost instantly under the doctor's normal gaze, and when he takes her into his office to examine her, there is nothing abnormal about her undressing. This is what she came for, and the doctor is performing his duty. Hypnosis has only precipitated a situation that has nothing unusual about it, and the rapport has reinforced it.

CRIMES BY PROCURATION

Trials of this kind always arouse a great deal of interest. At the time of the Gouffé case, a case of murder by procuration was being tried in the United States. At least it was believed to be murder by procuration. The defendant managed to free himself from his posthypnotic amnesia during the course of the hearing, and thus was able to reveal the name of the person who had suggested the crime to him. The instigator was hung. The details

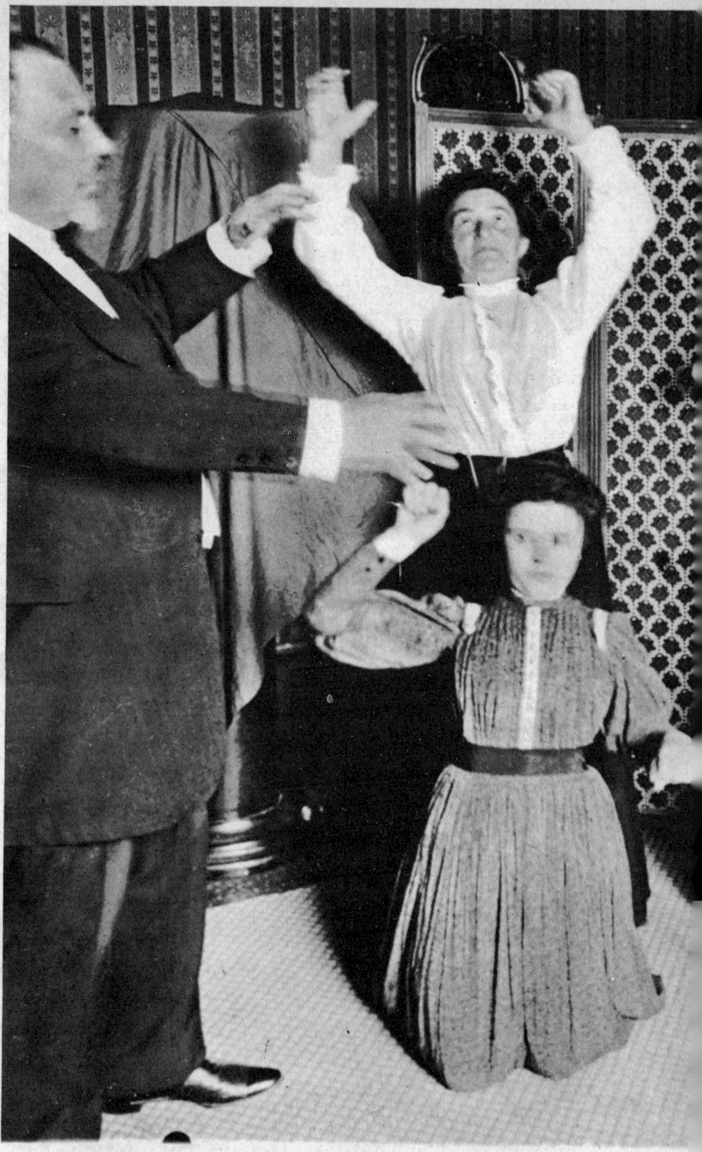

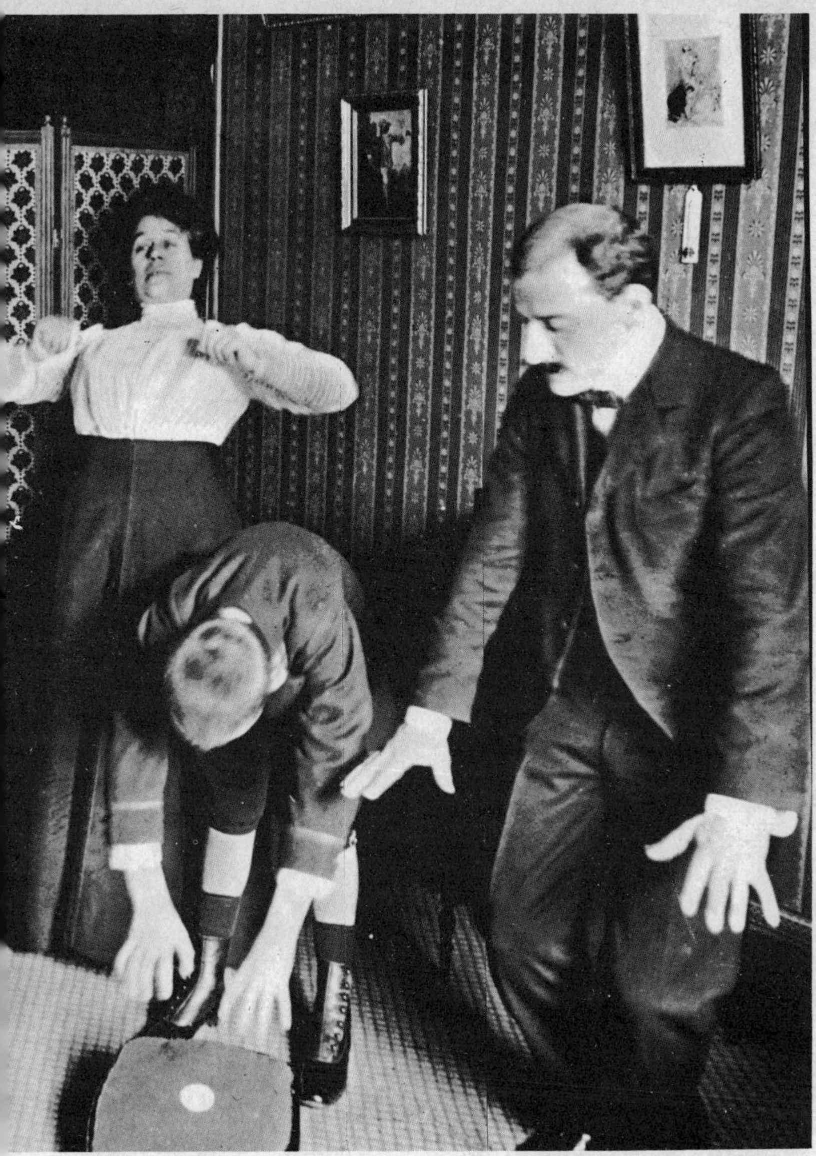

A parlor game conducted by a doctor in 1909. The hypnotized subjects cannot pick up the coin on the stool—*Roger-Viollet*

are vague. It all happened on the western frontier, where procedure and justice were improvised and men were impetuous, so nothing is clear from this verdict. The defendant could have been simulating, or the jury could have been making use of an excellent opportunity to get rid of an undesirable type.

We live, however, in a century that is more meticulous and exacting. In 1936, Sweden was stirred by the Sala case, in which the power of one boy, only just of age, over a whole gang of young criminals was disclosed. Stockholm learned in amazement that its central post office had almost been dynamited and that the confusion that was to have followed the explosion would have been the cover for an attack on a bank located in the same building. There was even greater suprise when it was learned that the ringleader had subjugated and possessed several girls by suggestion, yogism, and hypnosis; that he had, in his own words, pushed a homosexual accomplice, who he was afraid would inform on him, to commit suicide by "a slow process of suggestion"; and that he had forced one of his gang to drink poison under hypnosis. It was discovered that the gang crimes were generally committed by procuration. The instigator was not necessarily present, being content to direct the crimes from a distance.

In Germany in 1937, a strange murder trial saw the instigator of a crime condemned to ten years in prison and his accomplice to one year, while the main perpetrator of the crime was acquitted. She was a young married woman who was brought under the power of a greedy scoundrel whose acquaintance she had made in a train. He had impersonated a doctor and for seven years hypnotized her without her being aware of it. After first suggesting that she was suffering from diseases that only he could cure, he followed with other suggestions directing her toward vice. Then came the order to murder her husband. The hypnotist had protected himself by an involved series of posthypnotic suggestions; it took the court's consultant nine months to unravel the maze. When he finally managed to rehypnotize the young woman, he was able to make her relate the facts. After his testimony, the facts appeared so damaging for the man that the famous lawyer pleading his case decided not to defend him.

The psychiatrist in charge of gathering the medical evidence,

Dr. Ludwig Mayer, published an account of the facts of the case and also described no less than twenty-one cases of crimes committed under posthypnotic suggestion.

These have been extraordinary crimes that attest to one person's possessive hold over another's intellect, although nothing seems to predispose it for a domination of this kind. A particularly disturbing example is the case of an American schoolteacher whose hypnotist was the principal defendant in a charge of arson with intent to defraud an insurance company. The hypnotist claimed that the schoolteacher had hypnotized *him*. So the real hypnotized subject—the schoolteacher—was given a severe sentence. The truth was not brought out until after he got out of prison. Meanwhile, a psychiatrist had started a laborious investigation at the request of the schoolteacher's parents, who believed that their son had been unfairly condemned. The psychiatrist had the exceptionally good fortune to be able to verify the results of his investigation: twenty-six years later he was able to re-examine the innocent prisoner under hypnosis, and discovered that his account of the events, relived through somnambulism, had not varied.

The interest of this case is twofold. First, it shows that a hypnotist can successfully claim that the roles were reversed. If the hypnotist instructs his victim not to contradict him, he will be obeyed for as long as the posthypnotic suggestion lasts—and some of these suggestions are indelible. Secondly, as the motive of the crime, namely procuring money for the instigator, was in no way disguised, it appears that the suggestion can be *direct* and does not even require the guise of good intentions.

DOMINATION OVER A MIND

In June 1954, Denmark was spellbound by a trial held in Copenhagen. Two men were charged with an armed attack that had been committed by only one of them. In March 1951, Paul Hardrup, a married toolmaker, aged thirty-one, had walked into a bank and demanded that the contents of the vault be handed over to him. When the teller and the manager did not obey, he killed them. He was arrested almost immediately.

Soon after, some men who had known Hardrup in the Horsens

prison where he had spent three years, from 1946 to 1949, pointed out that he had fallen under the complete domination of another prisoner, with whom he had shared a cell for eighteen months. This man, Bjorn Nielsen, was a laborer, aged thirty-nine, who, by exploiting Hardrup's mystico-idealistic tendencies, had brought him completely under his domination through yoga and hypnosis. Hardrup was persuaded that there was a spirit watching over him and guiding him toward the realization of his ideal: the creation of a Communist party in Denmark.

This state of mind is exploited in conspiracies. Most political assassinations are committed by weak-minded persons who have been made fanatics. Hypnosis is not necessary for this conditioning, but it can facilitate it. Nielsen saw an opportunity for personal profit in his fellow prisoner's dream. By encouraging and directing him, Nielsen managed to make Hardrup believe that he, Nielsen, was the spokesman for his guardian spirit, that his own demands were those of the "spirit," and that they had the sole purpose of creating the political organism desired by the "spirit."

When Hardrup was set free, he handed over to his former cellmate all his earnings that had been saved for him while he was a prisoner. Then, when he started working, he gave him his wages. Nielsen found him a wife and ordered him to marry her because the "spirit" demanded it. Poor Hardrup, still being led without knowing it, performed a successful holdup of a suburban Copenhagen bank in a state of trance. He brought back about $3,000. Nielsen took the money and developed another plan of attack, still under the patronage of the "spirit." We know the result of this one.

The psychiatrists in charge of studying the accused found that Hardrup, although intelligent, was insane and subject to frequent manic attacks during which one fixed idea took hold of him. This one dream would possess him, making him indifferent to everything else. He was also a captive of a whole network of posthypnotic suggestions, so he hid the truth by every means possible. He declared that he had had no accomplice, that he had stolen the bicycle that he used for his escape, and that Nielsen had never succeeded in hypnotizing him. This all proved to be false. The holdup had been planned with Nielsen, and the bicycle belonged to Nielsen.

A psychiatrist managed to make Hardrup relive all the important events of this strange case from the hypnotic sittings in which he had received the criminal suggestions right up to the double murder. Finally, at the end of the trial (which necessitated twenty hearings), Nielsen argued that Hardrup's insanity was proved by his belief that a spirit of divine origin guided his acts. The jury found Hardrup guilty but not responsible. He was committed to a mental institution, and Nielsen was given forced labor for life. He appealed this sentence, but the supreme court upheld it.

In his conclusion, the psychiatrist who examined Hardrup declared that even if Nielsen was not materially guilty of the double murder committed during the holdup, he was guilty of another murder: that of Hardrup's personality. One wise commentator, Alec Mellor, regretted that the Copenhagen verdict "was somewhat reminiscent of the frenzy of medieval magic," and insisted that the "idea of spellbinding hypnosis" should be banished so that hypnosis could be taken seriously as it deserved.

Taking hypnosis seriously means that none of its possibilities should be held back. Too much time has been lost through blindness, and we should not at any price lay ourselves open, through ignorance, to a disaster that the adversaries of hypnosis would take pleasure in exploiting, as this would set back future research indefinitely.

Should we tone down some of the facts or even bypass them altogether? Should we lead people to believe that crime by procuration is impossible? That no mind, however weak or unstable it may be, can be manipulated under hypnosis?

Indeed, we have pointed out with regard to political assassinations that crimes where there is an instigator and a weak-willed person are not necessarily due to hypnosis. Very often these are the result of keeping bad company. With this in mind, it still remains to be shown that hypnosis is not effective when the hypnotist suggests undesirable actions.

It would be dishonest to claim that hypnosis is a harmless game to which we can be a party without any risks. There is a risk, albeit a minimal one. Although the risk is only slight, serious practitioners advise that, in the interest of both, the hypnotist and his subject should never work alone together. One fact is sure: the criminals by procuration were all individuals who had no right to be practicing hypnosis. The conclusion is obvious: it is both useful and even beneficial for many of us to know if we are hypnotizable; and there must be sufficient qualified and responsible people to inform us on this point.

PART IV

THE USEFULNESS OF HYPNOSIS

CHAPTER XI

Self-Hypnosis

THE reader may have been disconcerted by the association between yoga and hypnotism in the descriptions of criminal cases in the preceding chapter. Although we were rather hesitant about making this association, it did seem justified, for this is one of the paths into which hypnosis is leading.

The Hindu philosophy of yoga with its ascetic practices was created in the fourth century A.D. by the sage Pantanjali. But Westerners have made a sort of physical culture out of it, which is less fatiguing than true yoga.

In some of its exercises and some of its consequences, yoga (or more precisely, the branch of yoga concerned with the body, its health, and its maintenance, *hatha-yoga*) resembles present methods of self-hypnosis and relaxation. In Europe "autogenic training" is the best known of these methods. Autogenic training is organized self-hypnosis, by means of a few simple exercises that help concentrate the consciousness on the condition and functioning of certain parts of the organism.

ÉMILE COUÉ, PHARMACIST

At the beginning of this century in France, Émile Coué (1857–1926) was making known his method of conscious autosuggestion. This method was very successful with the public, but was based on principles that were not approved in the scientific world. Coué wrote, "Free will, which we insist on so fiercely, always gives way to the imagination. This is an *absolute* rule," and he illustrated this statement with obvious examples:

It is easy for us to walk along a plank nine inches wide and thirty feet long, if it is placed on the ground. But if the plank is raised so high as to connect the twin spires of a cathedral, we cannot take two steps without falling. This is because the image of falling immediately becomes generated into its actuality in spite of the efforts of our will (and possibly because of them).

The name of a person or a word we are trying to call to mind evades us until we stop trying to remember it, and then it comes back to us by itself.

When we are learning to ride a bicycle, the fear of bumping into an obstacle makes us ride right into it.

The more we try to control an uncontrollable laugh, the more we laugh.

The insomniac who is bent on falling asleep tosses and turns and cannot fall asleep. If he resigns himself, and decides to stay calmly stretched out without worrying, even if he has to stay awake all night, he soon falls asleep.

"I want to, but *I can't."* All the above failures can be summed up by these words. The imagination, which is the force of the unconscious, always prevails, but imagination itself can easily be guided by autosuggestion. Just as the fear of falling will make a person fall, so the awareness of pain accentuates it. On the other hand, if you say to yourself, "My pain has gone," it can disappear. This direct method is still the most effective. Instead of opposing the idea—or the thing—that we want to be rid of, instead of confronting it head-on, it is better to discreetly introduce another element that will neutralize it or even terminate it by suppressing the undesirable.

Every thought solely occupying our minds becomes real to us and has a tendency to generate its own actuality.

No matter what disease one may have, the autosuggestion that "every day, I am getting better and better" will induce the unconscious to act on the organ that is causing the suffering. When it is a question of being cured, the key words are, "It is passing."

Who was Émile Coué? He was only a provincial pharmacist with no important contacts and no great influence. French medical groups shrugged their shoulders at him. His ideas were accepted more readily abroad. Charles Bauduin, a Swiss, demonstrated the psychic mechanism responsible for making Coué's principles become effective: the words "It is passing" have to penetrate the unconscious furtively "through the back door of the mind"; and they have to be repeated insistently, but quickly, so that the intelligence does not pick them up. Otherwise, the mere fact of thinking about it would help to preserve the state we want to be rid of.

The method consisted of three steps: suggestion of the idea of modification, unconscious gestation, and appearance of the modification. The accuracy of this approach has been established. Coué is now considered an initiator and the master of what was the second Nancy school.

WHAT IS AUTOGENIC TRAINING?

Schultz's autogenic training is derived from hypnosis, but he departed from its traditional methods in the sense that autogenic training is a method of rational physiological conditioning designed to produce a general psychobiological alteration in the subject in which all the manifestations obtained by slight hypnosis are made possible. This is obtained without falling back on psychological techniques to solicit the subject's confidence and urge him to lay aside his free will and let himself be influenced. So one of the principal objections against hypnosis is avoided, the hypnotist's control. Schultz's technique is "physiological hypnotization" or "self-relaxation through concentration." It aims at disconnecting the thinking brain from the rest of the organism. Consequently, as Paul Chauchard expressed so well, "Since the barrier of consciousness does not exist physiologically in the cerebral cortex, the control of voluntary muscles will also extend to the voluntary muscles."

The subject starts by attaining control over the voluntary muscles, since this is most familiar to him. Later, he progressively develops control over the circulatory system, heart, respiration, organs, and finally the head (for autogenic training is a therapeutic process). At his own home, twice a day, and never more than three times, the subject performs a progressively graded series of six exercises. After about three months the subject will be able to put himself into a state of perfect relaxation, followed by a sensation of heaviness in the limbs and a sensation of diffused heat. These sensations constitute two of the characteristics of slight hypnosis.

First exercise. The subject is lying down or seated with his eyes closed, and he is completely relaxed. He says to himself five or six times, to whatever rhythm pleases him best. "My right arm is very heavy" (the right arm if he is right-handed and the left arm if he is left-handed). Then he adds once, to remind himself of the basic goal of the entire training, "I am completely relaxed." This exercise lasts a few minutes, and then to terminate it the subject rapidly extends and flexes his arm, and takes a deep breath. After this, he opens his eyes again.

This exercise should be repeated for two weeks. If it is successfully carried out, the sensation of heaviness felt first in the arm becomes spontaneously generalized in all four limbs.

Second exercise. Once the general heaviness has been obtained (and checked by the doctor), the subject says to himself, "My right arm is very warm." It takes two or three weeks for the heat to spread all over the body in a generalization procedure similar to the way in which the sensation of heaviness spread. The subject becomes aware of it, but this is not a mere impression. It has sometimes been observed that skin temperature rises by five to seven degrees and rectal temperature becomes half a degree lower.

Third exercise. After this control of the blood vessels, which goes hand in hand with becoming warmer, comes the regulation of the heart or "heart consciousness." The subject becomes interested in the functioning of his heart and discovers that he can influence it. Sometimes he is able to accelerate or slow down his heartbeats considerably. One patient whose normal pulse was 76 was able to produce variations of between 44 and 144 heartbeats per minute while still in a motionless state and with no emotional trauma precipitating it. This exercise is continued for two or three weeks.

Fourth exercise. Control of respiration constitutes the fourth stage. It is not so much a question of controlling respiration as letting it function with no conscious effort. Schultz wrote, "We instruct subjects to abandon themselves to their respiration." This liberation causes marked, permanent changes in the respiratory rhythm. As a result, the preceding exercises now become more intense and show more noticeable effects.

Fifth exercise. The subject concentrates his attention on his solar plexus so as to integrate control of the abdominal organs with the other controlled organs of his body. He imagines that his solar plexus is "flooded with heat." It is common to observe an immediate relaxation of the intestine on X-rays. Moreover, the whole body is relaxed because all five exercises have been mastered. The subject now has a sensation of streaming warmth throughout his entire body, comparable to the heat of a bath and, as a matter of fact, Schultz's method was inspired by the psychiatrist Kraepelin, who had praised the bath as calming.

Sixth exercise. The subject concentrates on the phrase, "My forehead feels pleasantly cool." This corresponds to placing a cooling compress on the subject's forehead when he is immersed in a hot bath.

SPIRITUAL ASPECTS

The version of Schultz's method known by most people is one in which all traces of mysticism have been removed. Among the chapters that have been excluded from the original German edition of Schultz's book (*Das Autogene Training*), two dealt with its similarities with yoga. According to Jung, autogenic training seems better able to "break the conscious cramp" that prevents the subconscious from emerging. On the other hand, yoga, which is badly utilized by people of the Western world because they are tense or too active, runs the risk of strengthening the conscious will or stifling the unconscious instead of facilitating their common action.

Through autogenic training the organism is freed from the restraining action exercised by the thinking brain and, with the help of the induced heaviness and warmth, the subject rediscovers his own internal rhythm. This rhythm stems primarily from the movements of the heart and secondly from the movements of the lungs. And we must not forget the importance of the solar plexus, which is the "abdominal brain," and its action on the frontal region.

Autogenic training ends in a state of suggestibility comparable to slight hypnosis, which is by no means an ineffective stage of hypnosis. But the objection can be raised as to why a three-month training period is necessary, for the subject must not pass to the next exercise until he is sure of having mastered the preceding one. Liébeault sometimes produced the same result in just one sitting. What, therefore, is the advantage of autogenic training?

In addition to dispensing with the hypnotist, autogenic training will work on anyone. With Liébeault, it was often alleged that the sensations of heaviness and warmth were merely impressions and that his cures were only imaginary. But with autogenic training, the sensations can be verified. A thermometer can measure the temperature, the pulse rate can be counted, and the relaxation of the intestine can be seen on X-rays. The subject can be followed and guided.

There are countless proofs. In 1958, 15,000 patients had already been treated by this method. It is particularly indicated for asthma, angina pectoris, chronic constipation, tics, and, in general, anything treatable by hypnosis, including "painless" childbirth. Some of Schultz's associates even began by hypnotizing their subjects. Furthermore, like hypnosis, autogenic training is more effective when it is carried out in collective sittings. In people with unstable temperaments it can even develop their sociability, making their lives more pleasant and their work more productive.

We must add that the exercises in autogenic training can cause disorders in the organism. Thus it is dangerous to engage in them without medical supervision.

JACOBSON'S METHOD OF RELAXATION

In Schultz's method, phenomena experienced in the right arm alone become generalized throughout the whole organism. This method is as simple as the American technique called "Jacobson's relaxation" is complex. Jacobson's method is "mental relaxation, the starting point of which is control of muscular relaxation."

The treatment lasts from a few months to more than a year.

The subject, who is lying on a bed, forcefully flexes his forearm as though to contract his biceps. When he releases his arm, he is asked to take note of the sensation accompanying this muscular relaxation. Gradually, he learns to perceive this sensation after only a slight contraction and to discern the slightest muscle pressure, so that finally he can relax completely without any prior contraction. He proceeds in this way for every group of muscles, including those of the face, the tongue, the cheeks, and the larynx (by counting up to ten in a voice that gets deeper and deeper). Two or three sittings a week are necessary under the supervision of a doctor, plus one or two daily sittings at home lasting thirty to sixty minutes. The general relaxation, obtained easily after it has reached the face, causes mental activity to cease spontaneously, and the subject falls asleep.

This is the first stage of the training. The second, which is carried out with the subject sitting in an armchair, is called "differential relaxation" and it teaches the subject to distinguish between the muscles that can remain relaxed and those that must be tense.

During the third stage, the subject learns to distinguish which muscular tensions accompany emotions affecting him, for example, fear, distress, shyness, phobias. He can thus anticipate and reduce these tensions, and this will contribute to diminishing the emotion itself.

SELF-HYPNOSIS IS NOT WITHIN EVERYONE'S GRASP

Self-relaxation is a technique of the future, and it is likely that the method outlined by Schultz will be developed further. But the excellent results that have been obtained should not make us forget that self-hypnosis is as easy, and it is faster.

Braid hypnotized himself on more than one occasion and successfully suggested the disappearance of rheumatic pain. Professor Forel of Zurich also succeeded in hypnotizing himself, as did Coste de Lagrave, who was also able to influence himself by suggestion and thus get rid of his fatigue and mental depression. These were masters with a thorough knowledge of their science, and everything was possible for them. Today there are some virtuosos who can hypnotize themselves while carrying on a conversation. But it is not necessary to be a hypnotist to obtain results.

Self-hypnosis is as old as magnetism. Mesmer did not have to post a magnetizer permanently by the tree he magnetized on the rue Bondy. Nor did Puységur post one at the foot of the Buzancy elm. Once they had started the magnetic flow, the patients could take themselves toward their crises. When mesmerism became somnambulism, autosuggestion was added to self-hypnosis. Puységur's manservant would announce in advance the crises he would have and would describe the symptoms. Then, on the said day, they would occur just as he had predicted.

Self-hypnosis is not within everyone's grasp, although a subject who is put into a deep trance by a hypnotist can rehypnotize himself very easily. However, trance is not a goal in itself. The incoherent manifestations of somnambulism and its aimless, almost irrational phenomena are not at all what we are looking for. Self-hypnosis, judiciously conducted and directed, is not easy to achieve, and it is even more difficult to direct it into a therapy. This is specially true when the state of trance obtained is not deep, because then it seems that self-hypnosis demands more finesse. With the exception of experts, only a wise and lucid person can manage to obtain appreciable results.

Autogenic training represents a considerable development: the precise details that it gives have not been equaled by any other method. So this technique, which is commendable merely by virtue of the restrained methods on which it is based, is invaluable. But, by limiting it to a result often obtained by Liébeault in a few moments, we have to wonder if we are exploiting all its possibilities.

We would like to make the deep trance accessible to more people, for, if the slight trance is adequate for the majority of therapies, a much more advanced state of trance is required for surgery and truly painless childbirth. Autogenic training makes the slight trance accessible to everyone without the need of a hypnotist. What remains to be found is a technique that, with an operator if necessary, will allow all the advantages of the deep trance.

We have already stated that for patients suffering from a cardiac condition the deep trance could one day mean the difference between life and death. We are still far from knowing all the possible advantages of the deep trance and the handicaps that will be suffered by those who, through physical impossibility or cowardice, are not able to be induced into this state. But we are sure that in the future hypnosis will certainly be assigned many other objectives.

C H A P T E R   X I I

The Psychology of the Innermost Being

NOW, having reviewed the discoveries made by some investigators, we should be able to name future objectives. Unfortunately, we cannot do this. We are rather like explorers at the edge of a virgin forest. Is it wise to venture into such a jungle of undergrowth? The complexity of details has made hypnosis seem more complicated than it is. A heavy past continues to exercise its influence: investigators are trying to perform miracles in order to remain worthy of their great predecessors whose contributions to hypnosis were tremendous and whose illusions were gigantic. It is as if the somnambulistic miracles and the feats performed at Salpêtrière had pushed back the boundaries of rationality for subsequent generations. This obsession is evident primarily in the United States. Experiments successfully performed with willing students in the applied psychology laboratories of the large universities are very impressive, but, as the reports record results obtained with a subject who could be mistaken, by an operator whose senses are fallible, there is always a doubt.

Therefore, we have to distinguish between the findings of these laboratory studies and phenomena that have been obvious since the origin of hypnosis. For example, occasional insensitivity to pain: it has not yet been determined with certainty if this insensitivity is caused by a desensitization of the area where the pain is located, by an interruption of its transmission by the nerves, or by a decreased perception in the pain center of the brain.

We are sure that memory is affected by hypnosis. It has often been noted that a subject in a state of trance can remember things he had forgotten. It is almost as though the brain has a registering device on which every sensation leaves an imprint. These memory grooves can be deep or shallow, but only the most significant events can be recalled immediately. Under hypnosis, by concentrating our attention on one given point, we can recall details that were more lightly registered. Focusing on one given point is detrimental to viewing the overall picture, but for remembering a forgotten fact or the location of a misplaced object, it does have a certain usefulness. This ability to concentrate one's attention is also effective when it comes to retaining material. A hypnotized subject perceives any alteration, no matter how minute, in a given state of affairs much more rapidly than an individual in his normal state of lucidity.

The domination of the mind by one fixed idea can be exploited to make a subject vigilant, as was the case with the night attendants in a mental institution who, under hypnotic suggestion, would awake at the slightest movement from any of the inmates. Is it possible to use this power of attention to retain things that could not otherwise be remembered? This has not really been proved. It is possible, however, that the concentration involved when learning something under hypnosis, and the reinforcement of what has been learned by a posthypnotic suggestion to remember it in the normal waking state, will mean that it will never be forgotten. There are some examples of this, but research in this area has not been extensive. It is rather strange that no hypnotist has ever used this method of instruction persistently. Nor has it been proved that a hypnotized subject comprehends faster, works more rapidly, or learns better.

OVERCOMING STAGE FRIGHT

Stage fright, it is generally admitted, can be overcome by suggestion. We know that it is an anguish caused by the dread of failure and that it increases all the more as the subject becomes aware of it. It affects actors in particular, but can be found in almost all walks of life. Hypnosis can relieve various apprehensions and the consequent inability to carry out certain functions.

Here, too, the degree of the trance is an important considera-

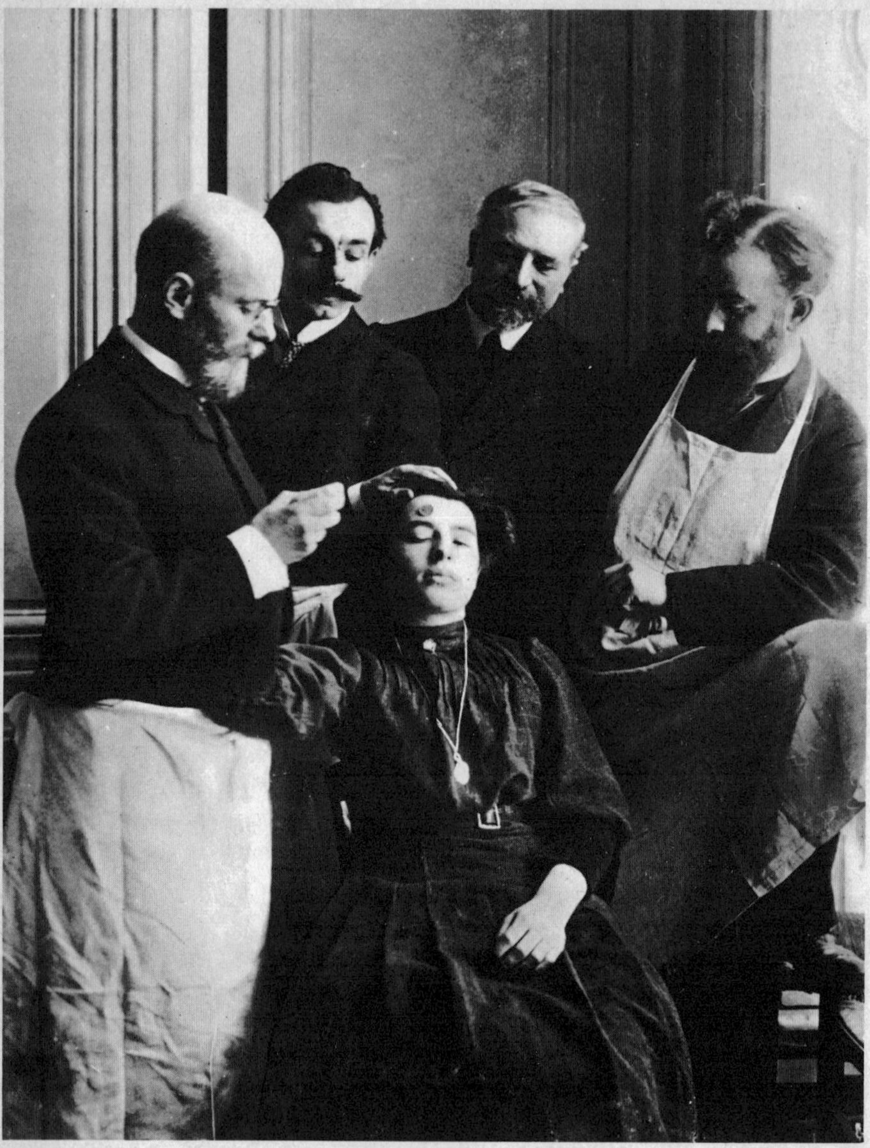

A demonstration of hypnotic sleep, circa 1900—*Roger-Viollet*

tion. We would not push an actor out onto the stage in a deep trance under the pretext of dispelling his stage fright. A deep trance would affect his critical judgment, and he would deliver a bad performance. Therefore, the subject is induced into only a slight hypnotic trance and given repeated suggestions that all will go well, that he will not forget anything, that he will not have any physical discomfort or apprehension, and that all his associates like him and wish him well. As a result, he will go on stage much more relaxed.

A more advanced stage of hypnosis is necessary to remove an inhibition. There are some offstage cases where we have full liberty to ease the restraint the subject has imposed on his consciousness. When the subject is not directly exposed to the public's critical eye, there are no objections to preventing him from exercising his own judgment and letting it yield to his spontaneity. The artist whose works are inhibited and hesitant can become very bold under hypnosis and throw himself into a fiery, colorful interpretation. The timid subject who always speaks softly can become bold and eloquent under hypnosis. Sometimes he can become too eloquent, as was the case with Puységur's somnambulist who did not hesitate to provide any medical diagnoses that were asked of him.

For a century, Finland has had a host of ecstatic women preachers. Aarni Voipio, their chronicler, sees them as hysterical women under the influence of self-suggestion. However, he notes that during the Camisard rebellion, in the Cévennes Mountains at the beginning of the eighteenth century, the front line of the rebels was composed of a host (eight thousand, according to him) of ecstatics of both sexes and all ages, all displaying similar phenomena: crises, convulsions, and amnesia. This would seem to indicate the possibility of self-hypnosis spreading by contagion and exaltation rather than by hysteria.

In another case, three hundred child prisoners at Uzès began preaching and wanting to save the souls of the doctors who were treating them. Some of the children were scarcely five years old. This is very young for such general hysteria to be manifested. On the other hand, we can assume that as a group, they had absolutely no sense of stage fright, and this resulted in a lack of critical judgment, turning them into moralizing little parrots.

INTENSIFYING SENSATIONS

Do the senses have a greater chance of being intensified than the intellectual faculties do?

When somnambulism was in vogue, subjects were believed to have such increased abilities to perceive everything "through the eyes of the spirit" that it would have been absurd to try and show that they were merely perceiving slightly better than people in the waking state. Consequently, interest was centered mainly on the way in which the sense organs could be affected, but rarely on intensifying them.

There are many examples where deafness has been cured by hypnosis, but possibly the hypnosis may only have influenced the obstinacy of a deaf person who did not want to hear. There are fewer examples of cures of farsightedness, but in many subjects it is difficult to determine the origin of the disease. There are many anecdotes about increased auditory or visual acuity by suggestion, but there have been few controlled experiments—and these are not very convincing. Their successes can almost always be attributed to increased attention. In his waking state, the subject is more inattentive, as is proved by his inability to hear all the ticks of a watch held within his hearing range.

One noteworthy fact is that the more rhythmic and mechanical the exercise to be learned, the better the memory remembers it. Kay mentioned the example of a tribesman who could recite by heart a missionary's entire sermon, even though he had not understood a word of it. The most influential works of ancient times, such as the Bible and Homer's poems, were known by heart long before they were transmitted from generation to generation in writing. Perhaps this accuracy of the memory in poetic incantations is based on hearing (the oldest of our senses) and on rhythm (the first stimulus) rather than on intelligence. Instead of studying the effects obtained by accelerating the playing of a piece of music, it would be more interesting to see if a subject who is not particularly musical can be made to remember the rhythms and their variations when he is induced into a hypnotic trance. It is possible that experiments of this kind could help distinguish between the role of intelligence and the role of nature. And so we would be able to make a distinction between two types of memory: one depending on the amount of interest devoted to the matter in question and the other resulting from harmony with our innermost being.

Could there be similar experiments for our other senses? It is doubtful. The senses of sight and taste are very capricious. Our five senses, which are connected (in a way that is not really understood) with our innermost being, function by comparing or estimating. These are cerebral activities. The faculty of hearing, however, relates what it perceives to standard phenomena, most of which are displayed in synchronism with the heart itself, from the first time that it began perceiving sensations. And so we rock a child's crib because this rhythm seems linked with the regular rhythms of our internal life. On the other hand, how many times have we had to verify what we think we have seen by touching it? The same type of verification is exemplified in babies who want to grab everything and taste it.

REGRESSIONS TO EARLY CHILDHOOD

Experimental regressions in time can be compared to the feats of the great period of somnambulism. The hypnotized subject is no longer told that he is traveling to another continent or to the moon but that he is once again an infant. And the subject regresses to this age in just a few moments. The experimentors are not disturbed by the fact that the subject, who is supposed to be no more than six months old, understands what they are telling him. They do not for a moment think that a child so young would be incapable of understanding what they want and therefore would be incapable of obeying their instructions to return to his normal age—and thus would have to remain regressed!

No one seems to have noted this detail, yet reports and articles never stop criticizing the circumstances of these regressions. The regressed subjects are tested to make sure that they have regressed to no more than the prescribed age. Then the incidents or scenes of childhood to which they refer are checked to see if they actually did occur.

Concentration of the memory certainly allows some subjects to remember forgotten details and, no doubt, permits them to relive distant events that are no longer part of their normal memory. But better proof than inkblot interpretation tests or childish drawings is necessary before we can affirm that hypnosis can obliterate everything from the brain so that the subject remembers nothing beyond his regressed age except the words that will terminate the regression. The inkblot tests and childish drawings could be done just as naïvely by individuals who are not hypnotized. Nor are the infantile gestures and intonations in regressed subjects adequate proof of absolute regression; lucid imitators can reproduce versions that are just as good.

These strange laboratory experiments are based on the undeniable fact that the memory of a hypnotized subject can sometimes recall past periods of his life in full detail. Another fact, generally admitted since Freud, is that our subconscious or unconscious bears the traces of events deeply affecting us at an age when we were unable to understand them. These traumas can influence our personalities in our earliest childhood and perhaps even before our birth.

By associating these two possibilities, some investigators have concluded that under hypnosis the patient should be able to remember his fetal life. Some subjects have even responded to this expectation. In 1953 in the *Journal of Mental Science,* Dr. D. E. R. Kelsey published the prenatal memories of a woman who, under hypnosis, recalled that her mother had used an enema nozzle to try to terminate her pregnancy during the sixth week. Going back even further, she remembered being ovulated and the painful impact caused by the ejaculation of the spermatozoa. One male subject remembered his own fertilization and also the discomfort caused him by his father's determination to continue his conjugal duties.

When supposedly serious investigators indulge in this type of experimentation, anything is possible. In 1956 in the United States, an amateur hypnotist, Morey Bernstein, engineered the hypnotic regression of a young woman who has given the assumed name of "Ruth Simmons" but whose real name was Mrs. Tighe. She related how in a previous life, at the beginning of the nineteenth century, she had been an Irish girl called Bridie Murphy. Her whole account was proved to be false. It was discovered that as a young girl she had learned all the Gaelic phrases scattered throughout her speech from an old woman. A book was written from her story and recordings were made, but the story collapsed before a film was made of it. However, it gave rise to thousands of meetings where people reincarnated themselves at will. One hypnotist even advertised that he could find a previous existence for any person willing to pay him a $25 fee, payable in advance naturally.

In the same period, a Dr. Tawney, desirous of the same success, published a regression going back five thousand years. One woman actually remembered having lived in Egypt under the pharaohs, three thousand years B.C. Seven hypnotic sittings, some introductory chapters, and the book was written, the first edition of which sold hundreds of thousands of copies. The alluring subtitle announced that hypnosis provided proof of reincarnation. The author was described as "The President of the National Association of Hypnotists and Therapists." The preface was written by Bordeaux, "Consultant Psychologist and Psychotherapist." Bordeaux himself was also the author of a work, and along with Le Cron from Los Angeles, he was credited with hypnotic induction in sixty fractionations (multiple rehypnotizations in one sitting)—a world record.

With hypnosis reduced to this, it is understandable why serious scientific groups in America frown when they hear the word "hypnosis."

OBSERVATIONS ON THE NOTION OF TIME

It is not untoward to assume that the word "regression" has no meaning. Because it suppresses or neutralizes, any kind of hypnosis is therefore a type of regression. It is plausible and perhaps even probable that under hypnosis we can recover lost memories and revive the psychological state of a given period. But it is very doubtful that we can go back to an intellectual level where everything we have perceived since that time has been obliterated.

The idea that Father Time can deliver the key to some of the problems of hypnosis is an old one. At the end of last century some serious experiments of a different kind were made, but they contain no affirmative conclusions other than that a hypnotized subject has a more accurate appreciation of time than a subject in a normal waking state.

It seems that the hypnotized subject is as conscious of the passing of time as when he is not in a state of trance. It seems, also, that in posthypnotic suggestion the subject's notion of time is more precise. This is not surprising, because the subject is called upon to pay attention to something that otherwise he would scarcely be concerned with. It is unlikely that firmer conclusions can be reached until physiologists can indicate more surely where the individual obtains his notion of time.

Are there two notions of time? One for evaluating the passing of hours and another for the passing of our lives? Why is it that an hour seems the same length whether we are adults or children, yet as adults one year seems much shorter? Our three-month vacation as school children seemed to last an eternity for us. Today three months are gone in a flash. Is this because the appreciation of "sixty minutes" is the result of an evaluation in our brain, while the impression of duration of time (three months, for example) is formed in another region? Perhaps the answer could be provided by hypnosis.

And so the ability to estimate time intervals is controlled either by reflection (which is responsible for evaluating the length of an hour), or by our notion of inner rhythm (which is responsible for formulating our impressions of relatively long periods).

DUAL PERSONALITIES

The fact that a notion that is evaluated as precisely as time can possibly be divided between two sectors of the nervous system leads us to the question of dual personalities. This was hinted at by the exponents of somnambulism. (But what didn't they think of in their feverish extrapolations?) Braid was so sure of the truth of this notion that he wanted to make the state of "double consciousness" the characteristic of hypnosis. In experiments Braid showed that a subject who had just come out of a trance was unaware of what he had done a few moments ago under hypnosis. But he could remember as soon as he was put back into a trance.

This double consciousness of subjects who have been induced into a deep trance was first studied in the last century along with dual-personality phenomena similar to those described in Stevenson's famous novel *Dr. Jekyll and Mr. Hyde.* In France, Azam, Pierre Janet, and Dr. Proust (Marcel's father) showed interest in this phenomenon. Dr. Chertok recalled that two navy doctors, Boussu and Burot, at the Congress of Hypnotism in 1889, reported a case of dual personality in a hysterical patient. Her treatment heralded Freud's cathartic method. We do not know whether Freud, who was in Paris at that time, heard this report —if he did not already know of it—because it had been published in a book prior to the congress. Nor do we know if such advance knowledge could have had any influence on his works.

Today this phenomenon, which is displayed during deep hypnosis, has nothing in common with the hallucinatory pathological state of subjects tormented by a dual personality. Hypnotists who obtain it do not consider it at all abnormal.

AUTOMATIC WRITING

Americans have thoroughly examined the phenomenon of dual personality, especially as manifested in what is called "automatic writing." J.-C. Filloux wrote that it is a question of "profiting from the anesthesia of a part of the body, especially an arm, to illustrate *various unconscious, but intelligent, acts in association with a psychic activity exerting itself absolutely outside of the principal consciousness."*

With a small amount of training, the hypnotist can make a subject sketch some graphic movements with his hand hidden from his sight by a screen. Then the subject will continue writing in a way that demonstrates that the second consciousness can remember (the subject may write reminiscences about past events) and is rational (the written text is coherent).

We know of a woman who compensated for a bitter loss by receiving messages supposedly from the beyond, thanks to this method of correspondence. For the American virtuosos specializing in the study of this phenomenon, both the content and the handwriting of these spontaneous texts written by an intellect more or less beyond control have revealed unexplored layers of the unconscious memory and very differing aspects of one and the same individual. The interpretation of the writings, either by the subject himself or, preferably, by a psychiatrist experienced in these matters, has produced fascinating accounts of the different personalities that one subject is capable of harboring in his subconscious.

In 1956 the record was twenty-three personalities in one subject. We do not know if this has since been bettered, but it is not likely, because Dr. Anita Mull, who was responsible for discerning all these personalities, was so proficient at cultivating a subject's talent for dissociation that she managed to make one subject read aloud while at the same time writing with both hands on two different topics.

The ability to write automatically was first attributed to hysteria, but today it is admitted that a large number of normal subjects could perform it. Professor Jean Lhermitte has shown that these disturbances stem neither "from a primitive functional division of the senses, nor from an original dissociation of what used to be called 'mental faculties' in the early days of psychology, but it is derived from an automatism elaborated slowly and patiently." He added, providing examples to support his statement, that when so-called spiritualistic practices are associated with automatic writing (as was the case with the woman mentioned above), very serious hallucinations can result, making life unbearable for the victim.

Investigators have not reported any observations of great interest or revealed aspects of the dual personality that would otherwise be unknown. But perhaps this exploration concerns an unfathomable part of the thinking personality, an area of which we have scant knowledge. This area is located in the folds of the cerebrum, and the work done by neurologists shows just how laborious and slow their investigations will be.

SPECTACULAR HALLUCINATIONS

Hypnotic hallucinations cover an extensive range, and have been greatly exploited since the period of somnambulism, especially by Charcot. Binet and Féré not illogically classified all successful fallacious suggestions under this heading. For example, if it was suggested to a subject that she was a peasant girl in a short petticoat, the subject began milking a cow and pushing away a suitor as though both the cow and the suitor actually existed. Then if this suggestion was immediately followed by a different one, for example, that she was an actress, she would display the imaginary gown she was now wearing at the hypnotist's instructions. These illusions can be continued after the trance by posthypnotic suggestion. The posthypnotic suggestion can be positive, "When you open your eyes, you will find a beautiful horse in front of you," or negative, "When you open your eyes you will not see the woman dressed in white; she will have gone." However, it seems that this is information imposed on the imagination and accepted by it, rather than hallucinations in the strict sense of the word. As a matter of fact, the hypnotist can obtain the same result without the subject opening his eyes, for example, by assuring the subject that a horse is alongside him and that he can hear the horse scraping its hooves.

All research in the field of illusions is very unrewarding. It is always difficult to prove the nature of the intervention of the senses and even more difficult to prove their affective disorder. When the hypnotist says to the subject, "You do not feel anything," there is, on the subject's part, inhibition and a refusal to feel. If the hypnotist asks him to touch a block of ice and tells him, "This stone is burning hot," it is not that the skin no longer perceives the sensation, but that the subject accepts a false interpretation of this sensation.

It is practically impossible to prove that a subject who has been made deaf by suggestion does not hear. This is also dangerous, because if the subject has not been told that he will be awakened by a tactile signal (or by a visual signal, if his eyes are open, the hypnotist takes the risk that the subject will not hear the command, "It's over . . . now you can hear!" This has actually happened, and legal action was taken against the hypnotist.

To sum up, we shall agree with Lhermitte that there are no hallucinations, only hallucinatory states. After all, it seems rather absurd to try to determine if a hypnotized subject who is shown a blank card and told that it is the picture of the President will

A practitioner of Voodoo—*Roger Viollet*

then be able to find it again in a batch of twelve other cards, all blank too. With regard to variations in residual magnetism, color, or disappearance-reappearance-transposition phenomena that can be attached to this experiment, the impossibility to control the results makes them very inconclusive. On the other hand, in order to further research and make the phenomena accessible to more people, perhaps we should try to reproduce experimentally the circumstances provoking certain strange reactions in mountaineers, who are generally healthy individuals in exceptionally good physical condition.

Through the danger and effort involved in it, mountaineering creates a special state in which one of the most curious manifestations is the impression of having a companion.

The English mountaineer Wilfred Noyce, who died in the Caucasus Mountains in 1963, gave a very vivid description of the phenomenon:

> It frequently happens to me, and I believe this is the case with many climbers, that I have the impression that there are two of us, especially when I am alone. Here I am really alone, in several senses of the word. One half of me looks around, criticizes the stumbling of the other, that awkward fellow, and remains out of the way and at a good distance from the physical conflict. These schizophrenic phenomena become more pronounced in high altitude climbs, as I observed at Pauhunri, in 1945. In my opinion, this state was the cause of Smythe's strange behavior at Mount Everest in 1933 when, alone at 8,200 meters, he divided a piece of peppermint cake in two and turned around to give half to his hypothetical companion. On the spur of a mountain, half of me is light and flies up the slope, asking why on earth it is chained to that laboring, breathless creature. The other half struggles on, pants and groans and tries to justify itself in the eyes of its superior partner.

Hermann Buhl, who climbed Nanga Parbat (26,660 feet), had the same illusion. The ascent took him seventeen hours, and he ended it "in a sort of hypnosis." While negotiating difficult passes, "the companion whom I never see, yet who is so familiar to me, never leaves me. The illusion becomes sharper in difficult places. And this idea comforts me and calms my worries. If I should fall or if I should slide, the other person will hold me with his rope. But there is no rope. There is no other person.

Then, a moment later, I know perfectly well that I am alone . . ."

Without trying to explain this phenomenon, let us point out two comparable phenomena. There was the case of an old maid who believed that whenever she went out she was escorted by a knight on a horse (and she even believed she could hear his armor clanking). Lhermitte attributed this illusion to the desire to feel protected. Ernst Junger, a German author writing about war, wrote that the confidence that we have in our own star makes us say to ourselves, "Nothing will happen to me," with the result that we only recognize how great the danger is for others and what little protection man has.

It is possible that the Himalayan climber experienced both these feelings. It is also possible that there are other causes. For example, perhaps the phenomenon is related to a child's invention of a playmate because he needs a spectator or a companion. In any case, when this does happen to mountain climbers, who are very carefully selected subjects, there is nothing unhealthy about it (unless exhaustion is a sickness) and there is certainly nothing hysterical about it (for if fatigue can cause it, then we are all hysterical).

Therefore, the companion phenomenon is a case of heautoscopy (vision of oneself by oneself), and not the result of any physical or mental unsoundness. It is unlike the numerous accounts of similar phenomena taken from the personal experiences of writers such as Goethe, Alfred de Musset, Lautréamont, and d'Annunzio. The details, which are well known, can be reproduced experimentally. This hallucination of having a companion is of interest because the state of great activity provoking it is exactly opposite to the absolute relaxation required by ascetic exercises.

Just as Schultz's method gives us our first rational insight into yoga practices, so by studying the Himalayan phenomena perhaps we shall have a better understanding of the journeys made on foot by holy men over the high plateaus of Tibet. According to Mrs. David Neel, these journeys are made under conditions so arduous that they leave us amazed, if not incredulous. Thus Hindu ascesis has two sides to it: both immobility (which Schultz elucidates a little for us) and overactivity (about which we know nothing yet).

THE MYSTERY OF LEFT-HANDED PERSONS

Is the ability to write with both hands, referred to in regard to automatic writing, really so strange (aside from the dissociation of thought, which permits many conjectures)? It seems that ambidextrousness is even natural. All anthropoids are ambidextrous. Only man is, as a rule, right-handed. It is generally concluded that this preference for one hand is related to speech. But after years of commendable research, Wilder Penfield and Laura Roberts are not at all sure of this, having carried out extensive investigations on the brains of trephined subjects (by local anesthesia) and on perfectly lucid subjects reacting to electrical stimuli.

Is a person left-handed by heredity, imitation, incompetency, or something else? When, at what period, did he start being left-handed? All these questions are still unanswered although they concern a phenomenon that is quite simple in spite of some bizarre exceptions. For example, many right-handed persons can blow their noses and wash themselves only with their left hands. It could be worthwhile to study under hypnosis the characteristics of this preference for one hand, perhaps by making the hypnotized subjects regress.

Dissertations on hypnosis do not devote much attention to uncontrollable laughter, aside from mentioning that the English call it "hysterics." Isn't there something visceral about uncontrollable laughter? And therefore different from intelligent laughter? Must laughter always be a reaction to something comical? Newborn infants laugh at a very early age, without having the slightest idea of what is funny. Their smiles when they are asleep—are they not reactions of pure content? Do they express the infant's animal satisfaction of finally being in harmony with an environment with which he cannot manage to familiarize himself? Is it because it helps protect us, so to speak, from the disorientation and problems of life that uncontrollable laughter, if it is not out of place, makes us feel contented? Uncontrollable laughter is physical laughter, not cerebral laughter. It is possible that uncontrollable laughter is related to those first bursts of laughter in our earliest childhood. This would explain why uncontrollable laughter can cause us to lose control over the reflex that took us the longest to develop, as it opposes a habit of fetal life—the sphincter reflex of the bladder.

It would also be interesting to know if tickling, which is light but rapid stroking on the surface of the skin, and which at best only allows a fleeting, imprecise intervention of the sensory mechanisms situated in the dermis, is related to uncontrollable laughter.

It is strange that uncontrollable laughter—and yawning, for that matter—plays no part in hypnosis, whereas a third contagious phenomenon, rhythm, also dependent or at least partially dependent on the nervous system, is so widely used in inducing hypnosis (metronome, passes, etc.).

RHYTHMS OF LIFE

The newborn infant has difficulty familiarizing himself with the world into which he is born. If the young child does have a semblance of consciousness both before and after birth, it is unlikely that this awareness can change radically from one day to the next. Yet this is what nature demands of him at birth.

Even puppies and kittens are more favored than man in this respect. Snuggled against their mother's belly, they can still perceive the rhythm of the maternal heart that had lulled them during their fetal existence, making it measured and harmonious. But once man is born and in his new environment, this sense of rhythm, which was vital until then, is not replaced. The baby is relegated to a crib, and his perceptive ear will hear only discordant, rhythmless sounds foreign to his life. From now on, and for many months, one entirely new sense must be developed: he must learn to rely on his sight. But can he rely on it? What does he rely on?

"It's a strange thing about my son," said an engineer. "He is so small . . . and already it seems that he is completely programmed." This is true, in the beginning at least. But since the child receives hardly any help, this does not last. The conflict begins. Everything seems to confuse his sense of sight, which the baby is not accustomed to and which gives him constant cause to be disturbed. The rhythmic vegetative existence within his mother is now far away.

When his cradle is being rocked, the baby is reminded of this prior rhythmic existence and he falls asleep soothed. But when he opens his eyes, nothing he perceives remains consistent. The food never arrives in the same way. Sometimes it is brought by someone dressed in white, at other times fed by someone in blue or red. The light changes and so do his surroundings. Nothing can be understood. His crib is moved from one corner to another. There are many voices and faces. There are a thousand things with no apparent reason. It is impossible for him to comprehend the incoherence of everything occurring around him and because of him. He inspects and verifies as best he can. He smiles when he sees something he can identify, something to which he has become accustomed, for example, his mother's face. He has finally found a point of contact with this world to which he can become adjusted through intelligence and reasoning, instead of being incorporated into it through rhythm. However, he will never be as well connected with the world through sight as he will through his ability to hear. Blind people, although more defenseless than the deaf in the struggle for existence, are nevertheless more serene. Deaf people are melancholy, moody, and anxious. They feel relentlessly cut off from this universal rhythm that the eyes are incapable of perceiving. What has been taken from them is not one of their senses; it is the ability of their whole being to vibrate in unison.

As he grows up, the child forgets his first confused impressions when he was born. Gradually he adjusts. His senses compel him to focus all his attention on a world whose boundaries never stop progressing. So he disregards his primitive being. This primitive being can sometimes be brought to the forefront through hypnosis, or it can rediscover itself of its own accord, for example, in collective gatherings where the contagion of rhythm is illustrated.

Some types of music exploit this special sensitivity to rhythm. First the rhythm of the music harmonizes with the primitive rhythm, then accelerates it, magnifies it, or goes against it and ends by creating a sort of vital, essential, animal frenzy that is also rather sexual. This liberation of the inner being, which is exemplified in many of the dances and ceremonies of primitive peoples, can also be found in the search by today's youth for even more accentuated rhythms. It is their way of reacting both against an existence that counteracts their fundamental nature and against domination by the mind. Yet we must resign ourselves to the fact that intelligence is responsible for our superiority. Our brain makes us what we are. It guides us, but we can guide it too—and hypnosis should permit us to guide it even more easily.

CHAPTER XIII

Hypnosis and Its Help to the Body

NOW that we have examined the influence of hypnosis on the intellect, we are ready to pass to the body. Most people believe that hypnosis affects the nervous system almost exclusively, that the intellect is its principal focus, and that, therefore, the body is only secondary. In spite of the enormous number of observations concerning the influence of hypnosis on the body, very few of them can be verified.

We have already spoken about "cataleptic" rigidity. In some hypnotized subjects, the body is so stiff that it can be stretched out between two chairs with the head placed on one chair and the feet on another without any other support. Placed in this position, the subject can support weights heavier than the weight of his own body. We have also seen that in a somnambulistic trance a weak woman threatened with rape can be endowed with the strength of an athlete, according to Binet and Féré. These are observations that were first made over a century ago, but they have never been truly verified, for no one has bothered to establish scientifically to what extent standard exercises performed in a state of cataleptic rigidity can be performed in the normal state. Nor has it been established how much greater the athletic strength of the somnambulist is, for example, in comparison to the strength sometimes provoked by desperation.

Facts of a physical nature can be established only by measurements, and conclusions can be drawn only from comparisons. Not long ago, studies were made to measure the two main aspects of man's physical strength. One of these aspects is dynamic (what man can accomplish by his strength) and the other is passive (what his resistance will permit him to endure). Because of the infinite variety of subjects, tests, and conditions under which the observations were made, it was impossible for the investigators to form generalizations, so the experiments lacked validity. Some individuals were strong, others were weak. Some were dextrous, others were clumsy. Nothing could be done to change this, so it made no sense to reduce so many variables to a common denominator.

The age of industrialization preceding this century forced investigators to re-examine the question of man's physical strength. With industrialization, a large number of workers were required to perform the same tasks for the same number of hours. Managers were interested in knowing what could be demanded of them and what their limits were. Studies were made measuring work and fatigue. These problems have now been the object of investigation for a century, but they are by no means solved yet, because most studies were aimed at determining the best conditions for increasing man's output. (It has been found that workers are most productive when their working conditions are good.) Furthermore, in most studies, the mental attitude of the workers distorted the research. No matter how detailed the investigations, the results obtained were always somewhat distorted, either through zeal or unwillingness, because of the conflicting interests of the two parties involved: the employer and the employee. Measuring man's capabilities using physical work as the yardstick remains an inaccurate and dubious method, since fatigue is a very subjective, highly individual matter. The fatigue of one muscle can be measured very accurately. But why does man become fatigued in advance (and in some way unfavorably conditioned) by the mere thought of performing a task he has no desire to perform? Why does this same man prefer to go out dancing than to rest after a day of strenuous skiing? We have no way of determining this precisely.

HYPNOSIS AND SPORTS

On the other hand, there is a field where work is a pleasure and effort a joy: sports. In many cases, sports activity can be measured accurately with a chronometer, so we are provided with all the comparisons we need. Unfortunately, as far as we know, these have not yet been used as the basis for a study of the physical effects of hypnosis. Methodical research probably has been carried out in the U.S.S.R., but our institutes have no knowledge of their results.

It is almost certain that hypnosis can be of use in sports. In the report on the use of drugs presented before the International Olympic Games Committee in Moscow in 1962, Drs. Ferreira Santos and Carvalho Pini included hypnosis in their list of undesirable stimulants and tranquilizers used in sports. It seems unfair to classify a process as harmless as hypnosis in the same category as the powerful "sympathomimetics," whose very name sounds forbidding. Hypnosis is none the worse off for being included in this list, but the mistrust in this respect will not make it easier to further our knowledge of it. This is a shame, because the use of hypnosis in sports should stimulate fruitful research.

A number of sportsmen believe in its possibilities. An eminent doctor, the director of a national organization with unquestioned authority, confided to the author that it was certainly possible to influence an opponent by fascination, particularly by gazing intently at the nape of his neck. Émile Anthoine, president of the French Walking Union and a former record holder in this sport as well as in running, admitted putting an opponent "into a complete state of inferiority, as though deprived of his strength." Under normal conditions, this opponent should have won. Anthoine also recalled how, through a transfer of cerebral energy, he convinced a runner who was losing to continue the race. This was Jean Vermeulen, who won the ten-mile world championship race at Manchester in 1914.

The first recognized use of hypnosis for athletes, quite obviously, is the suppression of stage fright. What is possible for artists is just as possible for athletes. Hypnosis that endows the painter with an assurance and self-confidence capable of altering his style completely can also reassure anyone who has doubts about his capabilities. We were not surprised to learn that it was for the highest-paid sportsmen, golf champions, that the first work was published claiming that a player could improve his game through self-hypnosis. Golf is a sport where nerves of steel are necessary for the approach shots. The mental tension and the knowledge that there are a thousand ways of ruining a shot make these final shots very difficult unless the player is a putting expert. Self-hypnosis can erase these fears in the same way that Coué's method removed the obsession that inevitably generated its own actuality. If the torment of "I am going to fail, I know it" is suppressed, the player will succeed.

Competent assistance should be able to improve on this personal therapy. A recent golf champion from England, James Hitchcock, admitted that his game had been very badly affected by his nervous depression. But he had regained his assurance following treatment from a London therapist, who asked him to stretch out on a couch and, by making passes over his entire body, from his toes to his eyes, made him sleep for twenty minutes. If this is not hypnosis, it resembles it sufficiently enough for us to mention the case. Similar attempts have been made in other sports with varying results.

The champion who is defending his title or the sportsman who must live up to the expectations of his fans is partly paralyzed by these obligations. This fear of disappointing is the price the popular player has to pay for the public interest that surrounds all sports. Suggestion should dispel this fear. It has been used experimentally on boxers, but suggestion itself cannot make a champion. By removing the boxer's apprehensions, however, it permits him to train calmly and to go into the ring with a confidence that he would not otherwise have. This is a great deal. Nonetheless, suggestion does not improve his intrinsic abilities, which will be the deciding factor in the outcome of the match.

Is it possible to develop these intrinsic abilities? This is questionable, as we lack both experimental data and comparisons between normal and hypnotized subjects. However, some champions are capable of making extraordinary efforts because they manage to sublimate all the pain of their fatigue. They can triumph in spite of the fatigue, or perhaps even because of it, if by self-suggestion they can succeed in transforming the painful symptoms of exhaustion into pleasurable sensations, thus leading them to victory. This is similar to the hypnotized patient who is told by his dentist, "As I pull your tooth, your insensitivity will increase." Dr. R. Bannister, who was the first man to run a mile in less than four minutes, also attributed his success to his ability to be insensitive to the fatigue. Many champions maintain that even during their greatest efforts they have never experienced any pain. It is as though success brings a point where *pain is no longer felt*. But this is such a subjective field that it really does not inform us about any possible increases in strength.

In the United States experiments have been undertaken to measure strength, and the efforts studied (the strength of one finger measured by an ergograph; the strength of a hand or an arm measured by the length of time that a subject can remain suspended from a bar) have given rise to varying observations. Generally, subjects under the influence of suggestion seem to have increased strength and resistance, but this is highly variable. According to Williams, the percentage of improvement in five subjects was between 1.6 and 52 percent. The average improvement was 16.08 percent. Can this improvement, resulting from the suggestion given to the hypnotized subject that he is stronger and does not feel the fatigue, create champions? We suspect that suggestion can increase resistance, but new resources cannot be created: the subject draws on what he has. However, in some competitive sports where the athlete does not have to draw on all his strength, if even a small improvement in his performance is possible because of a more dynamic concentration of his physical resources, and if he can assemble and expend all the strength he possesses in these few moments, this can be sufficient to change defeat into victory because the margin between competitors is often very slight. A few fractions of a second faster and a few feet ahead make a champion.

KNOWING HOW TO CONCENTRATE

Every sportsman knows just how necessary concentration is for him to be able to give his best performance. Before jumping, throwing, or weight lifting, the athlete musters and concentrates all his psychic resources on the physical effort he is about to accomplish. This is also true for all sports (although to a lesser degree). In every sport, the slightest distraction can compromise the performance. It is certain that hypnosis can eliminate distractions and make the subject focus his attention on what is essential. Can it do more? While monoideism is one of the most characteristic elements of hypnosis, we have no means of knowing whether this unthinking automatic concentration that is substituted for deliberate concentration constitutes an advantage or a disadvantage for the athlete if the exercise is limited to a brief effort that must be made just at the right moment.

It has been noted that deliberate concentration can have an identical effect to that of hypnosis. Jules Romain states that by prolonged sittings with his attention concentrated fixedly and precisely on the goal he wished to attain he managed, without self-hypnosis, to achieve by himself that disturbed vision that he had produced in hypnotized subjects. Since it can hardly be disputed that the faculty of attention is developed through hypnosis, research in this area could be fruitful.

In the case of a more prolonged, explosive exercise—for example, sprinting—another, rather obscure factor intervenes. This factor is the length of time during which the human organism can maintain itself at its maximum capacity. This time is very limited. Pushed to its utmost, the human machine expends its energy in less than half a minute. We do not know the exact reason for this, but it is confirmed by graphs of this expenditure. Pure speed in a foot race lasts barely more than two hundred meters. If this brief maximum capacity is due to the fact that the individual's internal rhythm is opposed, perhaps by modifying certain functions, as autogenic training does for the rhythm of the heart and respiratory rhythm, we could extend the length of time during which an individual is able to maintain his maximum speed. The gain of a few seconds is sufficient to make a runner invincible in middle-distance races. Obviously, this process would demand long and laborious training; a champion is not made in a few weeks.

One of the very few trainers who admitted that they resorted to hypnosis was the Australian trainer Forbes Carlisle, whose pupils Ilsa and John Konrads had broken many world records before they were fifteen years old. Carlisle admitted that he used hypnosis to persuade the youngsters that their capabilities were much greater than they thought. In short, it was simply a case of boosting their morale, and this was reinforced by the trainer's firm control over them—they were quite amenable because of their youth. When necessary, a more perspicacious will was substituted for their own during the race. Posthypnotic suggestion can also be used: "At this moment, or at this signal, you will do this."

ITS USE IN PHYSICAL EDUCATION

It is also possible to envisage an educational role for hypnosis in physical exercise. It is generally believed that education can be beneficial and effective only if the pupil's intelligence and will are developed and strengthened by the exercise. On the other hand, the development of reflexes and muscles loses nothing by being without thought.

Physical exercise is involved in the training of all sorts of automatic actions. Our basic movements are learned through training, and we learn them best when we learn them young. We have an unconscious gift for imitation (we could say an animal-like gift, since monkeys have it too), which is lost at a very early age. Consider, for example, the story of a little girl who had just learned to walk. Every time she held onto something with both hands, she contracted the muscles of her neck because she had seen her father do this when he fastened the gate to his estate. Later when the girl realized that holding was only a manual gesture, she no longer made a double chin. Thought had corrected pure imitation.

There comes a time when thought takes the upper hand, to such an extent that we can no longer truly imitate. As a result, some learning is no longer possible: for example, it seems that our sports abilities become definitely inscribed in us in about our twelfth year. The captain of an English cricket team published some very interesting observations on this matter. It appears that his athletic style had been completely developed by the age of twelve, and any attempts he made to improve faults in his style only made him less proficient. So he gave up using the corrected method, which he had practiced laboriously for months, and reverted to his own natural style that he had acquired as a boy, when he was capable of learning skilled gestures usefully. This is a very accurate observation that almost all sportsmen will confirm. We find it interesting because it indicates how useful hypnotic regressions could be in the teaching of sports. If regressions are what American psychologists claim they are, it should be possible to make an athlete with an imperfect style regress to an age prior to when these faulty movements were learned. Thus, he could be retrained following better principles.

LEARNING FASTER

There is nothing impossible about learning faster. Scott showed that conditioned reflexes are acquired more rapidly under hypnosis and that this conditioning persists when the subject returns to his normal state. New habits can be acquired under hypnosis because conditioning is easier than in the normal state, but the ability to learn is probably not increased. Developing an athlete means, first and foremost, developing automatic actions. The fact that this involves conditioning makes the procedure easier under hypnosis, and if, by chance, regression is possible (and we are not claiming that it is), the knowledge of one technique will not preclude the acquisition of another. "You are ten years old . . . you have never swum," the hypnotist will say to a subject who is accustomed to using the breast stroke and thus cannot accomplish the correct kick for the crawl.

Even if subjects cannot be made to regress, training them from a young age—younger than the age when learning becomes more difficult—would permit us to continue developing their reflexes until they are perfect. The ideal situation in training reflexes for sports would be the combination of a child's brain, which can assimilate all movements perfectly, and the muscles of an adult, which need no further development, for the movements learned in childhood, when the limbs are weaker, demand this development in order to be accomplished by the powerful muscles of the adult. This should be a fine experimental field for psychologists.

CONDITIONED REFLEXES AND TEAM SPIRIT

In team sports no deliberate, lucid action is possible unless the mind is directed by a whole series of conditioned reflexes that the player possesses for controlling the ball and moving according to the actions of the opponents. W. D. Furneaux, who has been conducting detailed experiments at London University for many years, has proved that the subjects who develop a conditioned reflex most readily are those on whom hypnotic methods have the most significant results. This does not mean, however, that they were the most easily suggestible. The best results do not necessarily follow from an effortless induction.

If individual sports demand many lightning reflexes, team sports require even more. In team sports a player's actions are determined not only by the opponents, but also by the movements, actions, and reactions of his teammates. If a player's movements are not automatic, he is outperformed. In trying to develop the spirit of a player, it seems that the results will be better if the subject is completely lucid. After all, the acquisition of an ideal, or, as in this case, a sporting ideal, is developed through conviction rather than suggestion. This is especially true where teams are concerned, because the qualities forming team spirit should be developed within the members, not imposed by an outside source, and should be instilled in the players through their common desire for fellowship and mutual cooperation. Some conditioning can certainly be useful in coping with an obstinate player who persistently makes the same error. Since a "conditioned reflex" implies a signal, it could also be easy, if necessary, to use posthypnotic suggestion to make this player consider a certain situation as a signal and to respond to it with the correct movement. However, we really believe that posthypnotic orders are as unreliable as suggesting to a shooter that he is going to hit the bull's eye every time. No game is stereotyped, and if certain reactions are imposed on a player, his performance will be compromised by a lack of flexibility. Even among players who are not hypnotized, if the instructions are too rigid they fail more often than they succeed. And what is the good of boosting the players' morale and giving them the will to win when a hypnotic state would destroy their most dynamic qualities? Some psychologists no doubt think that through a transfer phenomenon players will excel to please their hypnotists just as they would to please their fathers; but it is only in fiction that a player improves because of the presence of a person dear to him.

As a rule, the role played by hypnosis in sports is considered insignificant, but to us it seems important. Sports activities are a sincere testing ground of man's capabilities. And they are perhaps the ordinary individual's only defense against having his personality stifled by an era whose preoccupations are essentially mechanical, nuclear, and spatial—in short, everything but human.

CHAPTER XIV

The Domination of Crowds

WE admit that hypnosis may be able to influence man's intellectual and physical capabilities. But does each and every one of us want to know if we are hypnotizable? And if we are hypnotizable, what is the purpose of it?

If we believe that all is perfect and that our society and human affairs are fine as they are, then all we have to do is drift along with the march of progress. But progress is advancing at a fast rate, and before long it will overwhelm us with so many bodily comforts that some optimistic supporters of progress, predicting that we risk being crushed beneath its pleasant burden, want farsighted experimenters to give this runaway machine a more measured impetus.

Hypnosis can contribute to this aim, even if it is only to help in adaptation, which until now had occurred at random and without our knowing it.

We have observed that, with their dances and songs resembling incantations, the youth of today form a parody of primitive life. This phenomenon leaves many parents perplexed. Entangled in the web of progress themselves, the parents do not realize that young people today are more removed from nature than they were. They do not realize that life today is only restlessness and overactivity, even in our leisure hours, so that being alone in peace and quiet is a luxury that youth today has no familiarity with or taste for.

Individual cases may be an outgrowth of family problems, but the collective phenomenon is not. When young people gather together and create a disturbance, their outbursts are classified as manifestations of mass hysteria. As we have seen, "hysteria" is a very convenient term for classifying all the rather puzzling phenomena of nervous origin in man, animals, and especially in crowds. For example, when the workers at a wig factory in Hirson roll on the ground; when fans ransack a Parisian concert hall in honor of one of their idols; when Senegalese students set the embassy of their Moroccan ambassador on fire because they want higher student grants; or when Kenyan students have attacks of uncontrollable laughter lasting for one hour every morning, we say it is hysteria.

As the term "hysteria" has now been accurately defined, another word would no doubt be more convincing. However, let us assume, hypothetically, that the above examples are a form of hysteria similar to what Babinski called "pithiatism": the ability to display all the symptoms of a disease without being afflicted by it. So we could say that these attacks of mass excitement mimic certain diseases from which society suffers.

Unfortunately, the symptoms are vague and the group diseases to which we would like to relate them are even more obscure. Do they even exist? As a general rule, we tend to study the pathology of communities by sampling. Instead of viewing the social community as a whole, we isolate some of its constituents and question them one by one as separate individuals rather like the way in which Mr. Gallup conducts his surveys. Each person is asked to analyze himself, examine his "motivations," and express his intentions. This means according the person a voice in a process of which he may not have a full understanding.

FINDING OUR FREEDOM

On closer inspection and without even emphasizing the role of rhythmic excitation, which should, it seems, be distinguished from crowd reactions, we note that automatic movements are just as common as deliberate movements. Animals provide us with many examples of this: processionary caterpillars, sheep following after one another, and the migrations of many species and for many reasons, such as locusts, birds, bison, herring, eels, and salmon.

Of course, we are different. Our mind differentiates us from animals. It also makes us more susceptible to influence. Locusts do not have to follow fashion. Bison traveled from one end of the American continent to the other without being led off their route by arguments. They followed. We have to be convinced before we will follow. Is this preferable? The procedure by which we are persuaded to one action rather than another is more complicated, but we do follow. Like the bison, with thousands of cattle moving behind it, in front of it, and alongside it, thus influencing its decision, so with our freedom: millions of predetermined factors operating in succession leave us only a small margin for variations in our behavior. Basically we are more gregarious and conformist than locusts. They at least flock together only when there is danger for the species. Under normal circumstances, they fly at random. Humans do not have this independence of movement. And we cannot explain the reactions of social groups as a whole. In order to do this we would first have to define what is meant by a healthy society.

Is a society healthy when it is in a state of balance and stability and when its population hardly varies? Or is it healthy when there is constant movement of an ever-increasing population? The happiest people are usually those who live where the population density has changed the least. Perhaps we are living in a period of transition where man, realizing that individuality is not his ideal, is striving to attain a colonized state in which the individual can finally lose his personality, which is crushing him with its burden. What we would like to know is whether the normal state of communities is stability and harmony with their environment, or whether the normal state is expansion, characterized by "progress" resulting from the ability to expand at the expense of one's neighbors (by commerce or by arms).

If there are no norms and if we cannot assign a maximum population or an ideal mode of evolution to the human community, how can we discern anomalies in it? We have discerned very few: swarming (analogy with animals), panic and terror (extra-human origin), obsessional neuroses, merriment (mass exultation, which we are not familiar with in its pure state) are among the rare manifestations of anomalies whose particular characteristics have earned them a name. There are others. For example, we can have outbursts of fervor, enthusiasm, resentment, exaltation, ecstasy, etc., which are called "mass" outbursts even though they are only individual sentiments raised to a power proportional to the number of participants.

GROUP PHENOMENA

We know today that animal groups produce specific effects on each animal. These effects exert their influence on the pituitary and adrenal glands in particular. It has been noted that in cases of extreme overpopulation some species (locusts, tadpoles, mice, monkeys, deer) vary in build, fertility, and resistance to disease. It has also been established that some powers disappear in solitude.

This research has been extended to man, in studies made on pilots who were submitted to various mental and physical pressures. The studies showed that our species displays similar reactions. So we can assume that collectivity develops some faculties, inhibits others.

Some psychiatrists think that juvenile delinquency, characterized by young people gathering together in unprincipled gangs, stems from the fact that as prisoners of conformity, they have lost the desire to be alone. Consequently, instead of taking the form of an internal rebellion, the turbulence characteristic of adolescence becomes manifested outwardly in a belligerent way. And so, meditation, which is a human characteristic, is replaced by an animal tendency to assemble in groups where a minimum of thought suffices for the whole group. The mind abdicates its role, and the instinct to follow like sheep dominates.

This inhibition of the mind bears a similarity to hypnosis, and the comparison helps us understand some aspects of mass reactions. One sentiment displayed by hundreds of individuals together is much stronger than all the sentiments felt separately by the same subjects. Contagion is at work. The members of the group "mutually excite themselves." One thought in common is the only necessary ingredient to form them into a truly homogeneous group. Without this, they are a mob. But propose one simple idea to a crowd that is available and receptive (two of the conditions necessary for hypnosis) and it becomes cohesive because of this monoideism, which, in addition to being hypnotic, is also connected with our deepest instincts by its link with rhythm.

When these first three points have been established—availability, receptivity, concentration on one idea—the fourth will be easy. The crowd, awaiting a suggestion, will follow whoever wants to lead them. It is not necessary for the leader to be gifted with a special talent. After their attention has been focused on him, it is sufficient for him to hammer home one well-chosen point. It would be easy for a hypnotist to make his object the crowning purpose of this fellowship. He will have little difficulty becoming the image of the idea—namely the crowd's idol.

THE MAGNETISM OF LEADERS

The magnetism of the leader acts only as a means to an end. Once a group has been persuaded to congregate and pursue a common goal, a leader becomes necessary. Whether this leader proposes himself or is proposed, the group must put their solidarity behind him, making him their definition and realization of unity in a common ideal. Thus they show that he is the main support of the structure on which the group depends.

The more conspicuous the leader is, the greater his success. The domination he has established over the group will persist, and they will organize themselves around him. If he stays within their reach, he can do anything. Indonesia's President Sukarno, "flamboyant, tireless, and with a constant theatrical manner," offered a typical example of this phenomenon and showed that in crowd domination the essential factor is that the crowd must not lose sight of the focal point on which their attention has been centered. This person dominates their thoughts, and they eventually identify so strongly with him that they will accept any changes he imposes. He *is* the crowd. They see as he sees, and this will remain true for as long as he occupies the center stage.

We know that authority that is too strict often provokes resistance. Rebellious officers who attempt *coups d'état* gain the

A scene of hysteria provoked by the Beatles—*Agip*

support of their subordinates by promises or reasoning and therefore are not invoking hypnosis. But when a leader uses only his own prestige to be influential, then the hypnotic factor is at work. Pierre Boulle showed in *The Bridge on the River Kwai* a whole regiment being misled because their colonel had gone mad. The influence he exercised because of his position was maintained by his resoluteness in the face of their captors, and so the mass treason of the men, receptive and idle like anyone in captivity, becomes logical. This crazy colonel who made the infantry into an iron unit was followed without hesitation.

How many people in the confusion of a defeat or crisis have been reassured by one word? Peace . . . Independence . . . Reconstruction . . . Without taking a closer look, they adopt the leader in whose name this ideal has been proposed. It is the ideal that unites them and leads them into the venture. If necessary, technicians will be responsible for conducting it from the inside so long as the figurehead maintains his prestige.

INSIDIOUS ADVERTISING

It is inaccurate to classify the submissiveness with which a nation follows its leader without any critical judgment as neurosis, for this is a question of inhibition provoked by advertising, which fills the same role as the spoken word in individual hypnosis when a hypnotist maintains a patient's state of inhibition.

We are familiar with the methods of advertising. As in inducing hypnosis, the advertising instills into minds by repetition the need and desire for a given product. Domination, monoideism, idea generated into actuality: this is a procedure we are familiar with, but we also know that the unconscious rebels against too great an insistence. And so advertising currently resorts to a more subtle form of hypnosis, that of presenting only the outline of the idea it wants to convey. It is the consumer who takes control and rationalizes his own need for this particular article when, in fact, the advertisement has not even suggested that he acquire it.

Insidious advertising can penetrate "the back door of the mind" in a way that is completely without our knowledge. In a technique known as subliminal advertising, during the showing of a film a message can be superimposed for a split second on the normal image. The message is flashed so fast that the viewer is not consciously aware of it.

Ethical advertising agencies generally make it a point of honor not to impose upon the mental freedom of the public. Their advertising proposes; it does not impose. But what about subliminal advertising? Does subliminal advertising violate the viewer's free will? Opinions are divided, but advertising groups in England, two years after public experimentation with this form of advertising, have officially come out against it.

CHAPTER XV

Hypnosis, a Liberation

CROWDS are easy to handle, whereas individuals require a lot of skill. Humans will always disappoint investigators as long as they refuse to admit that the human machine is constantly being inhibited. It seems that this is the stumbling block for one of the most popular disciplines at the moment, conditioning. The advocates of conditioning would like to see human behavior, like that of Pavlov's dogs, completely defined by the interplay of conditioned reflexes. As yet, they have obtained only very inconclusive results with man. According to the Soviet masters (conditioning is almost a state doctrine on the other side of the Iron Curtain), the experiments succeed only when the subjects are not aware of the desired goal. "In order to obtain normal classical conditioning, the conditioning activity must be screened from the subject's consciousness, from his thought, and from all his mental processes," wrote J.-F. LeNy. If we suppress all the power of the mind we are doubtlessly close to a state of hypnosis and, inasfar as conditioning is desirable, it seems that hypnosis is also desirable, because it is able to facilitate this conditioning.

The fact that everything can be reduced to conditioning is expressed in the epigram: "Life calls the tune; we dance." But there is an abyss between this statement and an explanation of the whys and wherefores of our actions. And this abyss has not been bridged.

THERAPEUTIC UNCONDITIONING

Investigators have a lot of difficulty extending their research beyond the laboratory. With regard to unconditioning, their successes consist mainly of personality modifications by suppressing some usual reactions, unlike "brainwashing" techniques, which exploit the subject's emotions. The disorders of the nervous system and the terror and confusion that these techniques bring about are less reminiscent of Pavlov's methods than of the curses of ancient times made by preachers threatening their flocks with all sorts of torments both in this world and the next.

Associating pain with an action, and therefore as a penalty for the action to be suppressed is the most current application of Pavlovian methods. One English doctor, in order to cure a patient who had dissipated his fortune playing slot machines, obtained one of these machines and repeatedly made the sound of the arm being released coincide with an injection causing the player to feel nauseous. Thus he managed to create in this man the reflex to keep away from places where he would be exposed to hearing this noise that had now become very unpleasant for him. So the patient did not have to think of fighting temptation; his thoughts were directed at avoiding the cause of his nausea. But will this learning remain effective in the absence of a reinforcement, that is, in the absence of a reward (Pavlov's dogs were finally given their food)? The man's doctor was doubtful of this. The failure of countless remedies that provoke a nauseous feeling to cure habitual drunkenness leaves few illusions in this respect.

With conditioning, the results are even less clear. It is true that, as far as human "mechanics" are concerned, the only things we do well are what we do instinctively. The centers guiding our involuntary reflexes do not need to reflect. But unfortunately, in order to instruct them in what they must accomplish, we have to pass through the intellect first. "The perfect animal would have neither consciousness nor thought," wrote Paul Valéry. In fact, it would react automatically to everything it came in contact with. It could be conditioned without any trouble. Every meaningful gesture, however, implies an intelligent survey: observation, judgment, choice, imitation of a good model, and a reward that is the satisfaction of its success.

The complexity of one single movement in a sport—for example, shooting a goal in basketball—is such that its breakdown, when viewed in total ignorance with a view to learning it, goes beyond our understanding and we cannot conceive how so many factors could be conditioned.

What about learning a musical instrument? The multiplicity of movements needed to play a group of notes defies any attempt at programming without prior laborious instruction, And if, by chance, the development of a combination of reflexes like this were possible in a virgin intellect—an Australian aborigine, for example—still another form of training would be necessary: moderating the conditioned reactions to allow room for artistic sensitivity.

The limits to Pavlovian techniques are so evident that the supporters of conditioning are now trying to prove that training and conditioning are simply two names for the same thing. This combination saves us further research. We should only remember two things: that conditions similar to hypnosis can help obtain certain forms of human conditioning; and the flexibility of the word "conditioning," since it has become vague enough to be applied to everything that is learned.

ADAPTATION TO LIFE

Although we shall not have to use the word "conditioning" much more, we shall use it in the sense of "putting into condition," meaning optimal adaptation to the environment. This establishes the goal; whether this goal is reached "by establishing conditional relationships," according to Pavlovian doctrine, or by learning, training, education, or "conditioned" reactions, we do not care. For it seems obvious that hypnosis, which is capable of establishing a state of perfect obedience, should benefit all research pertaining to man's adaptation to his condition, especially because once the hypnotic state has been established, it can be re-established at a simple given signal.

Everything in modern life revolves around learning, and the

individual gradually adapts to his environment. However, it can happen that adaptation becomes physically impossible, for example, in long trips by air. The rhythm of life is disturbed because a change of climate is involved and because the regular diurnal rhythm is broken. Therefore a conditioning that would make the subject indifferent to these disturbances would be helpful. In France, Charles Jaulmes, André Bénitte, and Richard Lefebvre-Desnouettes have shown the importance of the alternation between wakefulness and sleep in these disorders and the less pronounced but well-established role of the endocrine glands, including the thyroid and adrenal glands. Our sleep and our glands can be influenced either by hypnosis or under hypnosis, and occasionally the functioning of some glands can be influenced by hypnosis alone. So its use is strongly indicated.

FORGOTTEN KNOWLEDGE

We cannot always condition exactly what we want. Reflexes are reactions to the outside world. Our knowledge of ourselves is dependent on the outside world and is affected by it. Hypnosis permits us to investigate warily what lies unperturbed within us. We investigate well only what we know. But how can we know nature, when we perceive only its effects? Therefore it is not without difficulty that hypnosis directs us toward recovering our unknown powers. But can we rediscover the sensory perceptors that our intellect has obliterated and that have been suppressed by the use of our powers of reason? Scientists do not agree on this. As a rule, it is believed that the judgment we exercise stems from our intelligence. But some believe that there are times when intelligence should not strive to comprehend it: sometimes we should concentrate as much as possible and at other times we should relax as much as possible and not think. Both these methods produce the safe effect. By concentrating on an idea in the first case, and by eliminating thought processes in the second, the result is a monoideism that induces hypnosis. Thus, the subject can display a clairvoyance, which is in no way magical and which exploits the ancestral treasure of our intuitive knowledge and the inexhaustible resources of our innate knowledge of life. This knowledge is simple, yet it has become sealed off from our cluttered intellects.

We perform certain unthinking yet beneficial actions that are comparable to the clairvoyance of a cat who eats grass because this is beneficial for it. But we no longer recognize these actions in ourselves. Perhaps the need felt by young children to go barefoot is one of these actions. Is this a means for them to make contact with the ground, since our habit of standing erect with shoes on our feet, acquired not so long ago, has deprived them of this contact? D. H. Lawrence wrote that it is civilization's great illusion to make us believe that we have outgrown the age of magic, the simple magic of touching. Children who take off their shoes and experience this magical contact perhaps know this better than we do.

But education soon imposes its shackles and weans children of this instinct to touch as it teaches them to stop putting everything into their mouths because they might poison themselves. Education does not distinguish between the reactions of the vegetative being, which has its own sensory organ, the skin, and the reactions of the senses, which are indispensable for the individual's survival, since his need to be informed is primardial. It is the vegetative being that takes off its shoes. But it is the individual made curious by the necessity to live who puts everything into his mouth in order to control his other sensory relationships through this most intimate sense of touch. This curiosity is indispensable for his education, as is almost all acquired knowledge.

It can hardly be contested that hypnosis can help us study the fundamental qualities of the species so that we may regain possession of our original natural powers, especially since the methods of accomplishing this are not clear. Defining the goals to be reached will remain a laboratory problem for a long time. An intimate knowledge of original human nature should help our civilized natures in adapting to the technological environment.

THE ROLE OF THE INTELLECT

"Thoughts are reflexes whose effect is suspended," wrote Sechenov a century ago (1863), and this is still a useful hypothesis. Hypnosis is often able to suppress a reflex, whereas the mind can only restrain it. What is the real role of the mind? It commands, defines, and gives direction to all our movements. Without this regulator, no action is exact, no gesture is precise. We are awed by the prodigious combinations of its thoughts. This represents the genius of the species. The intellect directs everything; nevertheless, it is not the vital impulse, not that explosive atom that can be awakened after thousands of years, for example, when a grain of wheat found in a pharaoh's tomb germinates.

The mind simmers, impatient to act. But the vital impulse derives serenity from its strength. It does not seethe; it constructs. It is the plant of life, robust and steadfast. Educational methods today disregard it. They waken it by overloading the mind with an alarming burden. When education starts taking into consideration the complexity of our nature, it will recognize that our equilibrium and happiness are dependent on this vegetative being that flourishes when the intellect is willing to ease its command. Education will have to define the roles of both these factors and find a simple means to achieve the essential, that is, letting the intellect and the vegetative being accomplish their respective missions. And so, liberated from the intense duties of the mind, which will now be undertaken by guidance machines, men will find in patience and serenity the path leading to a profound knowledge of their inner being and thus to an intimate understanding of and harmony with, the universe. It was by invoking this harmony that Mesmer recruited his supporters.

By means of a directed form of hypnosis, as perfected and as easy to practice in relation to present hypnotism as autogenic training is in relation to the Mesmer tub, each of us, if we wish to develop our natural powers, will be able to discover this inner vision revealing truth. At the same time, we will be aware of what becomes possible when the inner being can manifest itself without being opposed by the mind and when our vegetative system acts not in accordance with what the senses have perceived, but according to the instructions issued by its own powers of perception. Beyond this, man will methodically attain that spiritual level in which the body escapes its constraining forces.

This was the prodigious level to which the spiritual giants raised themselves.

Hypnosis, which is sedative by nature, stimulative when necessary, and capable of influencing reactions and controlling behavior, will no doubt be an instrumental factor in fashioning the world of tomorrow. What the form of this world will be is another question.

Let us not be pessimistic. Endowed with every power and afflicted with all human evils, Pandora still kept hope at the bottom of her box. She had hope in a better world where she would be free of that curiosity which had ruined everything for her. Hypnosis was the only gift Pandora lacked; so let us appreciate it.

APPENDIXES

APPENDIX A

Mesmer's Twenty-seven Propositions

1. A responsive influence exists between the heavenly bodies, the earth, and animated bodies.

2. A fluid universally diffused, so continuous as not to admit of a vacuum, incomparably subtle, and naturally susceptible of receiving, propagating, and communicating all motor disturbances, is the means of this influence.

3. This reciprocal action is subject to mechanical laws with which we are not as yet acquainted.

4. Alternative effects result from this action, which may be considered to be a flux and reflux.

5. This flux and reflux is more or less general, more or less special, more or less compound, according to the nature of the causes that determine it.

6. It is by this action, the most universal that occurs in nature, that the exercise of active relations takes place between the heavenly bodies, the earth, and its constituent parts.

7. The properties of matter and of organic substance depend on this action.

8. The animal body experiences the alternative effects of this agent, and is directly affected by its insinuation into the substance of the nerves.

9. Properties are displayed analogous to those of the magnet, particularly in the human body; diverse and opposite poles can also be distinguished and these may be communicated, changed, destroyed, and reinforced. Even the phenomenon of declination may be observed.

10. This property of the human body that renders it susceptible of the influence of the heavenly bodies and of the reciprocal action of those that surround it manifests its analogy with the magnet, and this has decided me to adopt the term "animal magnetism."

11. The action and virtue of animal magnetism, thus characterized,

may be communicated to other animate or inanimate bodies. Both these classes of bodies, however, vary in their susceptibility.

12. This action and virtue may be strengthened and diffused by such bodies.

13. Experiments show that there is a diffusion of matter, subtle enough to penetrate all bodies without any considerable loss of energy.

14. Its action takes place at a remote distance, without the aid of any intermediary substance.

15. It is, like light, increased and reflected by mirrors.

16. It is communicated, propagated, and increased by sound.

17. This magnetic virtue may be accumulated, concentrated, and transported.

18. I have said that animated bodies are not all equally susceptible; in a few instances they have such an opposite property that their presence is enough to destroy all the effects of magnetism on other bodies.

19. This opposite virtue likewise penetrates all bodies: it also may be communicated, propagated, accumulated, concentrated, and transported, reflected in mirrors and propagated by sound. This does not merely constitute a negative, but a positive opposite virtue.

20. The magnet, whether natural or artificial, is like other bodies susceptible of animal magnetism and even of the opposite virtue; in neither case does its action on iron and on the needle suffer any change, and this shows that the principle of animal magnetism differs essentially from that of mineral magnetism.

21. This system sheds new light on the nature of fire and light, as well as on the theory of flux and reflux, of the magnet and of electricity.

22. It teaches us that the magnet and artificial electricity have, with respect to diseases, properties common to a host of other agents presented to us by nature and that if the use of these has been attended by some useful results, they are due to animal magnetism.

23. These facts show in accordance with the practical rules I am about to establish that this principle will cure nervous diseases directly, and other diseases indirectly.

24. By its aid, the physician is enlightened as to the use of medicines, and may render their action more perfect, and he can provoke and direct salutary crises so as to control them completely.

25. In communicating my method, I shall, by a new theory of disease, demonstrate the universal utility of the principle I seek to establish.

26. Possessed of this knowledge, the physician may judge with certainty the origin, nature, and progress of diseases, however complicated they may be; he may hinder their development and accomplish their cure without exposing the patient to dangerous and troublesome consequences, irrespective of age, temperament and sex. Even women

in a state of pregnancy and during parturition may reap the same advantage.

27. This doctrine will finally enable the physician to decide upon the health of every individual, and to preserve him from the diseases to which he may be exposed. In this way the art of healing may be brought to absolute perfection.

(Mesmer's propositions as given in the English translation of A. Binet and C. Féré's *Animal Magnetism*)

APPENDIX B

Mesmer's Magnetic Tub

A TUB (or *baquet*) is a type of round, square, or oval vat. The diameter varies from tub to tub depending on the number of people who are to be treated around it. It has thick staves, assembled, painted, and joined together in such a way that it can contain about one foot of water. The upper part of the tub is about one or two inches wider than the base and is covered by a lid made in two pieces. This lid is mounted on the tub with its outer edge resting on the rim of the tub, to which it is nailed. At the bottom of the tub, some bottles are laid in convergent rows so that the neck of each bottle is turned toward the center. Then other layers of bottles are placed on top of these all around the circumference of the tub, with the base of the bottle resting against the side of the tub. Enough space is left between them for the neck of another bottle. Then a bottle is placed either upright or on its side in the center of the tub. With this bottle as the center, divergent rows are formed, first with half-size bottles, then with large bottles if this is possible. The base of the first bottle is placed against the center with its neck turned outward, and the base of the next bottle rests against the neck of the first bottle, and so on, so that all this layer of bottles have their necks pointing to the circumference of the vat. These bottles must be filled with magnetized water and tightly corked in the same way as the others were. It is preferable that this should be done by the same person. In order to give the tub more power, a second and third "bed" of bottles is placed on this first bed. But generally, the second bed is made starting from the center so that it covers one third, one half, and then three quarters of the first bed. The tub is then filled with enough water to cover all the bottles. Iron filings and powdered glass and other similar substances can be added, but I have mixed feelings about these.

Mesmer, *Aphorisms,* # 296

APPENDIX C

A Short Account of Former Methods of Inducing Hypnosis

PASSES

Mesmer's method: Mesmer put his hands on the subject's shoulders, then brought them down the arms to the extremities of the fingers. After holding the thumbs for a moment, he placed his hands back on the subject's shoulders again and repeated this process two or three times. He then touched the seat of pain with his fingers or with the palm of his hand, maintaining contact with the patient throughout all this handling.

Deleuze's method: "Sit opposite the patient on a slightly raised seat so that his knees are between your knees and your feet are beside his." Ask him not to think about anything, hold his thumbs with your fingers, and fix your gaze on him. After two to five minutes, release his thumbs, raise your hands to his head, place them on his shoulders for one minute, and then bring them down the arms with a light stroking movement. Repeat this pass five or six times, then make other passes, without contact, from the face to the pit of the stomach. Then place your thumbs on his stomach for about two minutes, with the other fingers below the ribs. Then make passes down to the knees and even to the feet if this can be done without difficulty. Similarly, passes are made down the spine to the knees and feet.

PASSES AND WARM BREATH

Esdaile's method: The subject was put to bed in a darkened room, and the hypnotist directed him to go to sleep. Then for an hour or more, if necessary, he made passes over the entire body and from time to time breathed gently upon the head and eyes. The preparation for a major operation lasted about ten days.

FIXED GAZING

Braid's method: Contemplation of a bright object (generally his lancet case) held about a foot from the patient's eyes, and at such a distance that fixed gazing would engender fatigue. Braid then brought his free hand toward the patient's lids, forcing them to close.

After a time Braid abandoned the method of fixed gazing and the patient was instructed to close his eyes at an early stage of the proceedings. Hypnotizations performed in the dark and his successes with blind persons convinced him that the influence was not exerted through the optic nerves. Hypnosis, he concluded, was the result of associations of ideas and imagination and nothing could be achieved without the cooperation of a subject who was willing, prepared, and aware of what was expected of him.

VERBAL SUGGESTION

Liébeault's method: "After asking the patient what he is suffering from, he makes him sit down, places his hand on the patient's forehead and without even looking at him, says: 'You are falling asleep.' Then, almost immediately, he closes the patient's eyes, assuring him that he is sleeping. He lifts the patient's arm and tells him: 'You cannot lower your arm.' If the patient does lower it, Mr. Liébeault pretends not to notice. He then makes the patient rotate his arms, telling him that he will be unable to stop this movement. While saying this, he rotates his own arms rapidly, even though the patient still has his eyes closed and he starts speaking continuously in strong and ringing tones. Then the suggestions begin . . ." (Delboeuf, *Le Magnétisme animal*).

Bernheim's method: After first making explanatory suggestions to remove the patient's fears, Bernheim followed the same procedure as Liébeault, asking the patient to think of nothing but sleep and describing the first symptoms the patient should be experiencing. Like Liébeault, he did not try to convince the patient that he had slept but wanted to assure him that the hypnotic influence could be exerted in a very short time without sleep.

FIXED GAZING AND PASSES WITH CONTACT

Doctor Philips' (Durand de Gros) method: The necessary conditions are local warmth, artificial light, and a sedate, confident hypnotist. The patient is invited to look steadily without blinking at a bright object placed in his hand and to concentrate his attention and his thoughts on the visual impression. After fifteen or twenty minutes, the hypnotist closes the patient's eyes, if he is not already asleep. He then takes the patient's right hand in his left hand, and with his other hand rubs the patient's eyelids, then his forehead. These actions are like an assertion of authority, and at the same time they establish contact between the patient and the hypnotist. Then he tells the subject that he is unable to open his eyes, etc.

SENSORY EXCITATION

The Method of Charcot's school: "Any excitation causing fatigue is susceptible of provoking hypnosis in suitable subjects. Thus we can agree with Dr. Richer in saying that all the methods are good provided that they are applied to a willing subject. Sensory excitations produce hypnosis in two ways: when they are strong and abrupt, and when they are weak and prolonged" (Binet and Féré, *Animal Magnetism*).

HOLDING THE THUMBS AND PASSES WITHOUT CONTACT

Charles Richet's method: The patient sits in front of the hypnotist, who takes the patient's thumbs and squeezes them firmly for three or four minutes (a procedure revived by La Fontaine and Deleuze). He then makes passes with outstretched hands in front of the patient's eyes as though he desired to close them.

HYPNOGENIC ZONES

Pitres' method (from Bordeaux, 1848–1928): In addition to the usual procedures, he used the methodical application of pressure on the hypnogenic zones defined empirically by Mesmer and by various physiologists, including Purkinje (1787–1869) and Laborde (1831–1903), who invented rhythmical traction upon the tongue in cases of asphyxia. The principal zones are the forehead, the top of the head, the root of the thumbs, the areas adjacent to articulations, the hypochondria, and the ovaries.

✓ USING THE WHOLE RANGE

Bérillon's method: Replace the subject's tension with a state of relaxation by the use of the "tremulant armchair." Absorb the patient's attention by letting him listen to a monotonous noise or a metronome. Place a blue lamp in a reflecting mirror about seven inches above the patient's forehead. When the patient's visual fatigue is manifested by blinking, he is told to repeat quietly several times: "I feel very calm; I am relaxing; I am not interested in anything."

✓ FRACTIONATION

The method of Grossman (1894) and Vogt (1902): The hypnotized subject is awakened and rehypnotized several times. Each time, it is suggested to him that he will fall into a trance more rapidly. The aim is to make the subject familiar with the induction procedure by repetition.

NOTE: In these very brief outlines, we did not deal with the important influence of contagion. In fact, the ideal method is to operate with a mixture of new subjects and subjects who have already been hypnotized. The sight of some subjects in a trance facilitates the induction of others. Mesmer, Liébeault, Bernheim, Philips, and Wetterstrand (from Stockholm, whose method employed fixed gazing, passes over the eyes, face, and arms, and pressure over the region of the heart) all took advantage of collective hypnosis.

APPENDIX D

The Stages of Hypnosis

LIÉBEAULT distinguished six stages of trance. Before Liébeault, Braid had set forth an even more concise classification. He distinguished only the attenuated stage (slight hypnosis); deep hypnosis, which he subdivided into two conditions, first alert and then apathetic; and finally, the hypnotic coma. Today a similar summary gradation—the slight trance, the medium trance, and the deep trance—suffices for most experts. But for persons who are not familiar with the characteristics of each stage, this division is too schematic.

The same objection was raised against Liébeault, so the stages he described were increased. His friend Bernheim divided hypnosis into nine degrees, and he was surpassed by two Americans, Davis and Husband. In 1931 they published a graduated scale comprising twenty-three stages, in which an uninfluenced subject was classified O while one in the deepest trance was classified 30. The scale developed by Lecron and Bordeaux, also Americans, is even more divided, comprising fifty different stages. The disadvantage of these overprecise gradations is that certain phenomena do not always occur in the sequence stated. For example, it can happen that the patient's inability to open his eyes, which Bernheim lists as the second degree of his classification, often "can only be obtained after catalepsy has been suggested and produced and automatic movements have been induced. These are Bernheim's third and fourth degrees. It is good for the hypnotist to be warned of this, so as not to ruin the induction by challenging the subject" (Dr. Géraud Bonnet). So a less rigid classification seems preferable. In the margin alongside Liébeault's classification, we have added some important phenomena that he did not mention.

LIÉBEAULT'S CLASSIFICATION

LIGHT SLEEP

1. Drowsiness characterized by lethargy, somnolence, heaviness of the head, difficulty in opening the eyes.	Slight trance
2. *Light sleep:* the beginning of catalepsy. The subject can still alter the position of his limbs by an effort of his will.	
3. *Deeper light sleep:* numbness, catalepsy, automatic movements possible. The subject is unable voluntarily to terminate suggested automatic rotatory movements.	Medium trance; "glove" anesthesia
4. *Intermediary light sleep:* in addition to catalepsy and automatic rotatory movements, the subject ceases to be in relation with the outer world. His attention is fixed solely on the hypnotist, and on waking he remembers only what the hypnotist tells him.	Personality changes; illusions of touch, taste and smell

SOMNAMBULISM, OR DEEP SLEEP

1. *Ordinary somnambulistic sleep:* characterized by complete amnesia on waking, and hallucinations can be induced during sleep. The subject has no memory of the hallucinations on waking. He now exhibits automatic obedience to the hypnotist.	Deep trance; illusions of sight and hearing
2. *Deep somnambulistic sleep:* characterized by amnesia on waking. Both hypnotic and posthypnotic hallucinations can be induced. Absolute submission to the hypnotist.	Regressions

APPENDIX E

A Sixth Sense: The Epidermic Sense

WE know that the only sense stimulated by direct contact is the skin. The sense of taste is stimulated only after the sense of touch, and the senses of sight, smell, and hearing do not come into direct contact with the excitant.

Of the five senses, the sense of touch is the easiest to fool. It discriminates badly, sometimes being incapable of differentiating a burn from a cold sensation. No doubt this is why the importance of the skin is often underestimated. But this error, which can easily be made by a sensitive surface so weak that its detectors, situated in the dermis, function by evaluation (a psychic phenomenon), should not permit us to infer that all the epidermis, which functions by conduction (a physical phenomenon) is just as fallible.

As a matter of fact, the epidermis can accurately evaluate sensations of atmospheric heat or coolness without any confusion. It is extremely sensitive to light, and its excitability is so indispensable that a frog whose cutaneous sensitivity has been destroyed falls into a coma and stops breathing. Therefore, we have to wonder if the epidermis is not perhaps the best equipped of our senses and the most easily influenced because it is dependent on the autonomic nervous system and not on the intellect.

The epidermic sense (if we admit that it exists) would therefore be the first sense to start functioning, as it makes the fetus sensitive to the warmth of the womb. The second utilizable sense in the fetus is hearing, which perceives the rhythm of the mother's heart. The other senses are exhibited only after birth. It has been noted in hypnosis that hearing is the last to be affected by hallucinations.

Therefore, we should establish a distinction between the sense of touch and *the evaluation of the environment by the epidermis,* because the inner being has been trained in this latter respect since his fetal life and it literally becomes vitally important after birth.

For if the newborn infant could not perceive by the sudden chilling reflex the difference between the liquid in which he was bathed in his mother's womb and the very different environment into which he has just entered, he might not take that first breath on which his existence depends. The fact that he will take this first breath whether it is dark or whether there is no noise shows just how much more important epidermic perception is than hearing or sensitivity to light (rather than sight).

The skin has more extensive powers than is generally believed. In some blind animals, such as the earthworm, sea louse, and nephargus (a sort of crustacean found in caves), the skin is sensitive to light. Jules Romain, the famous author of *Hommes de bonne volonté* ("Men of Good Will"), felt that man had analogous possibilities (disturbed vision), whose value he emphasized thirty years before Soviet research confirmed the accuracy of his observations. Perhaps the epidermis is also sensitive to sound: certain grating noises can provoke "goose flesh," which is a reflex contraction of small muscles close to the surface of the skin.

So little is known about the skin. We know how palpation and examinations by touch are effected through rather large, unevenly distributed corpuscles situated in the dermis and specialists have mentioned "points" of warmth, cold, and pain, but not in detail. We still do not know if the skin has secretory nerves "physiologically but not anatomically proved by the existence of perspiration" (*Physiologie,* Binet and Roger, Volume 10). Nor do we know if there are nerves responsible for the nutrition of the tissues; and the nature of the nerve endings, which are the center for itching sensations, remains problematical.

In short, the epidermis is a large area of tissue abundant with nerves not yet identified, and whose functions are still mysterious.

A P P E N D I X F

Chronological Table: From Magnetism to Hypnosis

1766	Mesmer presented his thesis on medicine in Vienna.
1773	Mesmer performed his first cure with the use of magnets.
1778	Mesmer arrived in Paris.
1784	Puységur discovered magnetic somnambulism at Buzancy.
1784	Condemnation of animal magnetism by the Royal Commission.
1812	Creation of a mesmeric hospital and a department of magnetism in Berlin.
1813	Deleuze published his critical history of animal magnetism.
1814	Faria discovered the fascination technique.
1819	First dental extraction performed on a magnetized subject by Martorel, a dentist in Paris.
1820	Dupotet practiced magnetism in the hospitals of Paris.
1829	Cloquet amputated the breast of a woman who had been magnetized by Dr. Chapelain.
1831	Husson's report in favor of magnetism.
1837	Dubois' report condemning somnambulism and magnetism.
1838	Elliotson, president of the Royal Medical and Surgical Society of London, professed belief in magnetism.
1841	At Manchester, Braid demonstrated that the "magnetic fluid" was a myth, and gave hypnotism its name.

1842 In London, Dr. Ward amputated the leg of a subject who had been magnetized.

1845 Amputation of a leg at Cherbourg by Drs. Loysel and Sibon. The magnetizer was Durand, a philosophy professor.

1846 Without ever having witnessed magnetism, Esdaile successfully performed his first operation in Calcutta (in two sittings, April 4 and 11).

1848 Grimes proved the so-called phenomena of electrobiology in the United States.

1853 Durand de Gros made electrobiology known in France and stressed suggestibility.

1860 Broca and Velpeau spoke to the Academy of Sciences about hypnotic sleep.

1866 Liébeault published his book on provoked sleep.

1875 Charles Richet gave an account of his research on somnambulistic phenomena.

1876 Claude Bernard asked the Biology Society to investigate Burcq's metallotherapy.

1878 Charcot gave his first large demonstration at Salpêtrière.

1886 Bernheim published his book *Hypnotism*. The German edition had a preface written by Freud in 1888.

1903 Pavlov described conditioned reflexes to the Congress of Madrid.

1910 Coué gave up his pharmacy at Troyes in order to devote himself exclusively to the propagation of his method of conscious self-suggestion.

1925 In the United States, Burgess presented his classification of the stages of hypnosis in dentistry.

1925 Schultz developed autogenic training.

1929 Jacobson published *Progressive Relaxation* in Chicago.

1935 Flanders Dunbar introduced psychosomatic medicine in the United States.

1944 Read published his book *Childbirth Without Fear* in London.

1952 At East Grimstead, near London, Mason obtained a 70 percent improvement in a case of congenital ichthyosis.

1954 A law was passed in England prohibiting all public demonstrations of hypnosis.

1958 The American Medical Association acknowledged the therapeutic value of hypnosis.

1962 A brain operation was performed under hypnosis in Indianapolis; the neurosurgeon was Som N. Nayer; and the hypnotist was Paul Brady.

APPENDIX G

Index of Names

Franz Anton Mesmer

Hypnotism began with Mesmer (1734–1815). He tried to link up the use of powers possesed by the human being with the science of his time, which had been stimulated by the discovery of the law of gravitation. Some points of his doctrine of animal magnetism bewilder us. Others are becoming clear only today. Although it was ultimately a failure, and in spite of its faults, his written work deserves to be praised. In it he predicted future discoveries, and even some errors that would result from these. The solicitude shown by Napoleon, who granted him a pension, and by Frederick William III, who invited him to Berlin to teach, was not unfounded. By his intuition, Mesmer was a giant.

J. P.-F. Deleuze

Born at Sisteron in 1753, died at Paris in 1835, Deleuze was a naturalist at the Museum of Natural History. He was in constant contact with Antoine-Laurent de Jussieu, who was the only member of the committee appointed by Louis XVI to examine animal magnetism to have successfully magnetized. Deleuze practiced magnetism for the first time in 1785 at Aix. The publication of his *Critical History of Animal Magnetism* in 1813 was an important factor in reviving practices that had been condemned for thirty years. Quoting as his authority the Puységur brothers, who defined magnetism as "physical action in which the soul intervenes," his work was still, according to some authors, the best to be found a century later. He is the only author of this period whose study of ESP (extrasensory perception) phenomena, as described by the magnetizers of the mesmeric era, can be trusted.

Dupotet

Jean de Sennevoy, Baron Dupotet (1796–1881), was the first nonmedical practitioner of hypnosis to work regularly in hospital wards. Deleuze by his masterly *Critical History,* Faria by his demonstrations, Bertrand by his lectures, and others had given a new impetus to animal magnetism. But it was Dupotet, who, at the age of twenty-five, was responsible for exploiting the possibilities of magnetism in hospitals. Husson and Récamier at the Hotel-Dieu, and Georget and Rostan at Salpêtrière were inspired by him. Dupotet directed the long investigation performed by Husson in the name of the Academy of Medicine, and he was the person most affected by the condemnation of magnetism in 1837. It was he who led the English doctor Elliotson to investigate the subject. Throughout his life, this man, responsible for the first renaissance of magnetism, remained an ardent supporter of it, and before he died in 1881, at the age of eighty-five, he was able to witness the triumph of hypnotism.

Armand de Puységur

Grandson of a field marshal, Armand-Marie-Jacques de Chastenet, the Marquis de Puységur (1751–1825), was a colonel at the age of twenty-seven. He and his brothers were among Mesmer's most enthusiastic disciples, supporting all his undertakings. At Buzancy, he magnetized a tree and obtained results different from those observed with Mesmer's tub. The subjects became drowsy and, without experiencing a crisis, passed into a state that he called "somnambulism," during which they exhibited clairvoyance and exceptional powers. Although Armand de Puységur, an excellent magnetizer, used passes, his doctrine could be summed up by: "Believe and be willing." A man of great integrity and extreme generosity, he was the mayor of Soissons and died at Buzancy in 1825.

John Elliotson

Elliotson, the son of a pharmacist, was born in London in 1791. He was educated at Edinburgh and Cambridge and graduated as a doctor of medicine in 1821. A nonconformist, a spirit of progress permeated Elliotson's whole being. In 1831, he was appointed professor of medicine at London University, and he is said to have been mainly responsible for the erection of the university hospital. He was the founder of the Phrenology Society and president of the Royal Medical and Surgical Society of London. It was after Dupotet's visit to England that Elliotson began investigating magnetism. As a result of official opposition, he resigned his position rather than give up his convictions. He founded *Zoist,* a journal that was published quarterly for thirteen years. Highly regarded by some (Thackeray dedicated *Pendennis* to him) and constantly attacked by others, he pursued his work in magnetism until he died in London in 1865.

James Braid

Born in Fifeshire, Scotland, in 1795, Braid received his medical education at Edinburgh. After practicing there as a mining surgeon for some years, he moved to Manchester, where in 1841 he witnessed La Fontaine's experiments in magnetism. At first skeptical, he was convinced at the second sitting, and gave his first lecture on magnetism six weeks later. He gave the name "hypnotism" to these phenomena and was the first to attribute hypnosis to mechanical causes and to employ strictly physical induction procedures. Although he was criticized both officially and by other magnetizers, Braid did not stop pursuing his investigations until he died, on March 23, 1860. Azam had introduced braidism into France in 1859. In Germany, Heidenhain, who introduced Pavlov's theories, repeated Braid's experiments but did not mention him in his work (1880).

James Esdaile

Esdaile, son of a clergyman, was born at Montrose, Scotland, on February 6, 1808. He studied medicine at Edinburgh and after graduating in 1830, was employed by the East India Company and was given an appointment in Calcutta in 1831. During a two-and-a-half-year leave of absence for health reasons, he visited Egypt and Italy. In 1838 he returned to his duties at the native hospital at Hooghly, about twenty-five miles north of Calcutta. He had never seen hypnotization when in 1846 he attempted to relieve a convict's pain by operating on his double hydrocele under hypnosis. Encouraged by the success of the two operations on this patient, Esdaile went on to perform an incomparable series of operations, totaling several hundred. A mesmeric hospital was placed at his disposal by the government. He left India when his period of service expired and returned to Scotland to retire (1851), but later moved to Sydenham, where he died of a lung ailment on January 10, 1859.

Ambroise-Auguste Liébeault

Liébeault, the son of a farmer, was born at Farrières (Meurthe) on September 17, 1823. He had intended to enter the priesthood, but instead studied medicine at Strasbourg. While a student there, he read a book on animal magnetism and then successfully mesmerized several subjects (1848). He received his M.D. in 1850 and shortly afterward started practicing medicine at Port-Saint-Vincent, eight miles from

Nancy. In 1860, at the same time that Velpeau was communicating Azam's experiments to the Academy of Medicine, Liébeault began experimenting seriously with magnetism, treating any willing patients free of charge. In 1866 he published his book, but only one copy was sold. He then went to live in Nancy, and with the help of Bernheim founded a school whose reputation became worldwide. His method was based mainly on suggestion, but he did not formally condemn the fluid theory. He died at Nancy in 1904.

Hippolyte Bernheim

Born in Mulhouse in 1837, Bernheim studied medicine at Strasbourg. In 1868 he settled in Nancy and became a professor in the Faculty of Medicine. In 1882, Liébeault cured an obstinate case of sciatica that Bernheim had treated in vain for six months. In consequence of this, Bernheim went to see Liébeault and his work. Gradually Bernheim was convinced, and he became a zealous supporter of the new therapy. Two books published in 1884 and 1886 made him famous. Then he attacked the Salpêtrière school, whose "deep hypnotism" (*le grand hypnotisme*) he claimed was only a "cultivated hypnotism," practiced on a few hysterical patients. He compared it to Liébeault's "slight hypnotism" (*le petit hypnotisme*), which was effective without producing spectacular phenomena. Subsequent hostile reactions forced him to resign his position as the head of the school. He died in Paris in 1919.

Charles Richet

Born in Paris in 1850, Richet was the son of an eminent surgeon. In 1875, preceding Charcot, while studying medicine in Paris, he had methodically studied somnambulistic phenomena, which he provoked by making passes over his subjects. In 1884 he expressed his conviction that no one is absolutely immune to magnetism. He was appointed professor of physiology in 1887, received the Nobel Prize in 1913 for his discovery of anaphylaxis, and became a member of the Academy of Medicine and the Academy of Sciences in 1914. He was interested in aviation, wrote an important literary work, and all his life pursued the scientific study of "metapsychic" phenomena. He was in more or less permanent disagreement with official scientific bodies when he died in Paris in 1935.

Pierre Janet

Nephew of Paul Janet the philosopher, Pierre Janet was born in 1859. After graduating from the Ecole Normale Supérieure, he collaborated in Charcot's work at Salpêtrière, where he directed the psychology laboratory. His experiments in telepathic suggestions, performed at Le Havre with Dr. Gibert in 1886, attracted attention. He received his doctorate in literature in 1889 and his doctorate in medicine in 1893. In 1902 he became a professor at the Collège de France and was elected a member of the Institute in 1913. An agnostic, he was the most eminent member of the Salpêtrière team to rebel against the systematic negation of hypnotic phenomena, which he believed had a curative power limited to certain types of patients.

Jean-Martin Charcot

Charcot, the son of a coach builder, was born in Paris on November 29, 1825. He received his education at the Lycée Saint-Louis, then started working as an intern at Salpêtrière in 1852. His thesis was accepted in 1853, and he became a hospital doctor in 1856. He was accorded the title *agrégé* (licensed to teach in colleges and universities) in 1860. A wealthy marriage and influential connections allowed him to give Salpêtrière a radiance that it had never had before. Charcot founded no less than five medical journals. He was a member of the Academy of Medicine (1872) and the Academy of Sciences (1883). He became interested in hypnotism after witnessing a demonstration by the Belgian hypnotist Donato. The exploitation of hypnotism at Salpêtrière together with the team's research on hysteria became very well known in Paris and elsewhere. Unfortunately, their work was spoiled by the patients' lack of sincerity and the futility of some of the research. Charcot died of pulmonary edema on August 16, 1893.

Ivan Petrovitch Pavlov

Born in 1849 at Ryazan, where his father was a priest, Pavlov was influenced at an early age (1863) by his reading of Sechenov's *Reflex Actions of the Brain*. After his medical studies at St. Petersburg, he spent two years on detached service, mainly at Breslau working under Heidenhain, whose work showed hypnosis to be a purely physiological phenomenon. In 1890 Pavlov became director of the physiology department of the Institute for Experimental Medicine in Leningrad. Pavlov was awarded the Nobel Prize in 1904 for his work on the physiology of the digestive glands, and in 1903 at the International Congress of Medicine in Madrid, he had described conditioned reflexes for the first time. Until he died in 1936 he continued studying the cerebral hemispheres, and in particular his research was centered on physiological mechanisms and higher nervous activity, in which he discovered a number of hypnotic phenomena.

J. H. SCHULTZ

Born in 1884, the eighth child of a theology professor, Schultz first exhibited a great love of animals, then an eclecticism that predisposed him to music, sports, and literature as well as biology. His medical education, begun in 1902 at the Physiology Institute of Göttingen, where he was influenced by Max Verworn, was completed at Jena in 1907. He specialized in psychiatry and had the opportunity to follow Hans Bergen's research on cerebral waves before becoming director of a psychiatric hospital with two thousand beds during World War I. He began his own research on hypnosis in 1905 after reading Freud and Oscar Vogt. The latter showed that the therapeutic value of autosuggestion did not reside in self-persuasion but in the induction of mental states analogous to hypnosis. This was the path of experimental research followed by Schultz at Jena, Dresden, and finally at Berlin, where he has resided and taught at the university since 1924. In 1932 he published his excellent work on autogenic training, dealing with the psychophysiological mechanisms and various technical possibilities of hypnosis (muscular relaxation; heaviness; dilatation of the blood vessels: warmth. Since then, his method has been perfected and has become widespread in its applications. Neurologists, hypnotists, and specialists in psychosomatic medicine show interest in it.

A. A. MASON

Born in 1926, Albert Abraham Mason was completing his medical education in London with a preference for psychosomatic medicine when in 1950 he heard about a case of congenital ichthyosis, which he decided to try to treat by hypnosis. The treatment was a rapid success, and the patient's improvement was so complete and so lasting that the Royal Society of Medicine warmly received his report, delivered in 1955. For the first time in the history of medicine, a structurally organic disease had yielded to a therapy. At about the same time (1955), the plastic surgery operation related in Part III Chapter 9 was performed. Even though a century separated them, this operation linked up with the major operations performed under hypnosis by Esdaile in Calcutta. Since then, Mason has worked in the psychiatric wards of West London Hospital and King's College Hospital, officially undertaking research on hypnosis in both hospitals. He is also the director of studies for the Dental and Medical Society for the Study of Hypnosis. Among other works, Mason published the first controlled study of a hypnotic treatment of an asthma case and a report on the effects of hypnotic anesthesia on the reactions of the cortex. In it, he showed that the blocking of pain by hypnotic analgesia takes place in the cortex, not at lower or intermediary levels where "the seat of the pain" was generally located.

APPENDIX H

Glossary of Terms

AMNESIA. Loss of memory; it can be total or partial.

ANIMAL MAGNETISM. The power derived from the universal fluid and contained within a living being.

AUTOGENIC TRAINING. A technique of self-hypnosis allowing certain functions to be regulated.

AUTOMATIC ROTATORY MOVEMENTS. The impossibility to stop a rotatory movement (generally of the forearms) once it has been started by the hypnotist.

AUTOMATIC WRITING. The unconscious action of writing, performed in a state of trance.

AUTOSUGGESTION. The actions of giving oneself suggestions.

CATALEPSY. A state in which the individual has no external sensitivity and cannot perform voluntary movements. It is usually manifested by a rigidity of the body or certain parts of the body. In this condition the body and limbs can keep any position in which they are placed. It can also be manifested by an excessive flexibility (*flexibilitas cerea*). By extension it can also mean suggested stiffness or numbness, for example, catalepsy of the eyelids (first stage).

CATAPLEXY. Stupor, often due to fear, that causes an animal to remain in any unusual position in which it is placed.

CLAIRVOYANCE (*or second sight*). Preternaturally acute faculty of perception, formerly associated with the state of somnambulism.

CONDITIONED (*or conditional*). Said of behavior acquired in reaction to environmental conditions.

CRISIS. In the early days of magnetism, the state of a strongly influenced subject.

DEEP HYPNOTISM *(le grand hypnotisme)*. The advanced stages of hypnosis, studied by Charcot in the hysterical patients at Salpêtrière. It includes somnambulism, lethargy, and catalepsy, but not necessarily in that order.

DOUBLE CONSCIOUSNESS. Dual personality. The individual is completely unaware in each of these states of what he did or felt in the other.

FASCINATION. The attempt to induce hypnosis by fixed gazing; its successful result.

FLEXIBILITAS CEREA. Flexibility comparable to that of soft wax. See *Catalepsy*.

HALLUCINATION. Illusory sensation with no external cause.

HYPNOIDAL. The state in which the first effects of hypnosis are felt.

HYPNOSIS. A particular state of the nervous system in which inhibition of certain areas allows unaccustomed action.

HYPNOTIC SLEEP. A state in which the subject, influenced by hypnosis, is susceptible to accepting a suggestion. (It is not necessary for the subject to be really asleep or even to have lost consciousness.)

HYSTERIA. A pathological state of the nervous system causing various disorders and simulating various diseases. Subjects suffering from hysteria are the most easily influenced by suggestion.

INHIBITION. A process impeding the subject's reaction to a stimulus or a group of stimuli. Inhibition is opposed to excitation, and its effect is one contrary to reaction. The term is occasionally used to mean "restraint"; in this case, it designates certain apprehensions that can be dispelled by hypnosis.

LETHARGY. A pathological sleep; a state of inaction. One of the stages of hypnosis, according to Charcot.

MESMERISM. Mesmer's doctrine; synonymous with animal magnetism.

MONOIDEISM. The domination of the brain by one single idea.

PASSES. Originally, the magnetic action exercised by hand movements (as opposed to the laying on of hands). By analogy, the action of rhythmic sweeping motions of the hands: luminous passes or thermal passes.

POSTHYPNOTIC. Is said of an effect that occurs after the hypnotization has been terminated: posthypnotic suggestion; posthypnotic amnesia.

PSYCHOANALYSIS. Exploration of the unconscious.

PSYCHOSOMATIC. The designation of a branch of medicine that accords an important role to the effects of the mind over the body.

RAPPORT. The bond linking the subject's mind to the hypnotist's mind.

REGRESSION. The state induced by hypnosis in which a subject relives a previous period of his life.

RELAXATION. Mental equanimity resulting from a general diminution of muscle tone.

SECONDARY STATE. A state of somnambulism in which the subject exhibits faculties that he does not ordinarily possess and reveals a second personality more gifted than the real one.

SOMNAMBULISM. A state of sleep presumed to be identical to that of somnambulists, who, while still asleep, act as though they were awake.

STIMULUS. A change in the environment of such a nature that it provokes specific nervous activity in the subject. "Excitant," an older term, has the same meaning.

SUGGESTION. Action on the intellect through the spoken word and the subject's subsequent behavior.

TRANCE. A particular state of unconsciousness or exaltation obtained in some hypnotized subjects. By extension, every hypnotic state: slight trance, medium trance, somnambulistic trance, deep trance, absolute trance (but not necessarily in this order).

TRANSFERENCE. Originally, the transmission of a spasm or a disease from one subject to another. In psychoanalysis, the transfer of a repressed feeling by the patient onto the operator.

UNIVERSAL FLUID. Originally, an imperceptible but active force exteriorizing animal magnetism. Today, "fluid" is used to mean a wave or radiation that cannot be discerned by regular physical methods.

YOGA. A Hindu philosophy accompanied by ascetic practices. People of the Western world are generally familiar only with the aspect of yoga that deals with the body.

INDEX

Index